Dear Dad,

I sure wish you could have made this trip with us! I'm praying for you daily for a speedy recovery. I thought this book might amuse you!

Take Care,

Love

Shannon

WINE IS THE BEST MEDICINE

WINE IS THE
BEST MEDICINE

Dr. E. A. MAURY

With a supplement on American wines
by Julius L. Jacobs,
U.S. editor of *Wine and Spirits*

translated by
Marie-Luce Monferran-Parker

SHEED ANDREWS AND McMEEL, INC.
Subsidiary of Universal Press Syndicate
Kansas City

Notice from the Publisher

We think you will find this book a lively and entertaining discourse on wine and what the author conceives to be its nutritional properties and its values as a supplementary medicine.

The book is not a "home medical adviser." Obviously neither we nor the author conceive of wines as curative or medicinal in and of themselves. The author suggests only that wines have value as a "supporting medicine."

Clearly anyone with a medical problem should seek advice from the health adviser of his or her choice, including the extent to which wine should be used as a supplementary medicine.

Copyright © 1974 by Editions du Jour
"American Wines for Health" Copyright © 1977 by Julius L. Jacobs

First published in France by Editions du Jour
First British edition published 1976 by Souvenir Press Ltd.

Library of Congress Cataloging in Publication Data

Maury, Emmerick A
    Wine is the best medicine.

    Translation of Soignez-vous par le vin.
    Includes index.
    1. Wine—Therapeutic. I. Title.
RM256.M3313 1977   615'.32   76-55751
ISBN 0-8362-0699-1

CONTENTS

Preface to the Second French Edition   1
Introduction   3

PART ONE: WINE IN NATURE

1. ANATOMY OF WINE   13

The Color of Wine   13
Notes on the Geological Composition of the
Soil of Origin   14
The Bordeaux Region   15
The Burgundy Region   16
The Rhône Region   16
The Jura Area   17
Provence   17
The Southwest   17
The Loire Region   18
The Champagne Area   18
Alsace   19

2. THE CHEMISTRY OF WINE   21

Wine and the Hippocratic Elements   22

The Mineral Elements   23
The Organic Elements   27
Tannoid Products   29
Enzymes   29

3. WINE AND VITAMINS   31

Oenotannins   32
Other Vitamins   33

4. THE PHYSIOLOGY OF WINE   37

Action on the Digestive Tract   39
Action on the Nervous System   41
Action on the Urinary System   42
Action on the Cardiovascular System   42

5. ALCOHOLISM AND CIRRHOSIS   45

PART TWO: WINE AS THERAPY

Introduction   51
Maladies   57

PART THREE: A MEDICAL LEXICON OF WINES

Introduction   109
Clinical Indications   111

Supplement on Other European Wines   115
American Wines for Health   121
Therapeutic Index   143

PREFACE TO THE
SECOND FRENCH EDITION

Within a single year the first edition of this book was sold out. I want in the first place to thank the discerning publisher whose foresight enabled the book to be published.

In France as well as abroad this essay on oenotherapy (wine therapy) has aroused great interest among lovers of good wine, who are a great deal more numerous than might be suspected.

Some reviewers in France made helpful criticisms of the book, which enabled me to revise certain pages and to expand the text for its second edition.

I hope that an ever increasing number of patients will be able to benefit from the natural therapeutic effects of a well chosen wine. And I hope equally that the vintners will take the point that it is in their interest to take even better care of their products, and to deliver to those who need it a wine whose qualities can be favorably compared with the best.

Note to the American edition. For the benefit of American readers, a chapter on American wines by Julius Jacobs has been added to the end of the book.

INTRODUCTION

Much has been written about wine since the beautiful spring day when Noah left his legendary ark to set foot on dry land after the flood, and planted a vine as a symbol of renewal.

However, scientists assure us (and of what can they not assure us?) that this plant—of the family *Ampelidaciae,* or as it is now more usually termed, *Vitaceae*—was already known in the Mesozoic era and that it originated in certain parts of Asia. Originally a wild plant, the cultivated and domesticated vine invaded the European continent in prehistoric times and the juice of its fruit served as a beverage for our remote ancestors. But the Biblical story loses none of its symbolic meaning for not being literally "true." Noah was probably quite tired of seeing around him, his people, and animals nothing more palatable than a liquid mass that tasted like mud. He therefore set out by cultivating a fruit altogether new to him, to create for himself and future generations a beverage worthy of man. And this beverage was WINE.

As Victor Hugo remarked in his *Contemplations,* "God made only water, but man made wine."

The origin of wine dates back to farthest antiquity, and it is, like the horse but in a different way, one of the noblest conquests of man. We find more than 450 references to wine in the Bible. In the Marriage at Cana, Christ changed water into wine so that the festivities should not be overshadowed by its lack. Later, this product of the vine was identified with His blood, and in due course consecrated as such by the Church. Since the first centuries of our era, and thanks to Christianity, the juice of the vine has become an indispensable element in Church celebration as well as in the duties of hospitality.

The records of ancient monasteries also remind us that monks have always been allowed to drink wine to brighten their meals on High Feast days. St. Benedict himself advised his brothers to drink a measure of wine with their monastic repasts so that their meals should "always remain digestible and cheerful."

In the period of progress in which we have the rare privilege of living, it has become on the other hand fashionable to condemn wine out of hand, in the name of a false conception of hygiene and dietetics. Wine is held responsible for a variety of ills, such as alcoholism, the increase in crime, and automobile accidents. Heaven knows, though, that in the history of humanity we have never drunk as much mineral water and fruit juice as we do today! But all the essays, learned lectures, radio and television talks by sad-looking experts concentrate on blaming wine—nothing in short has been spared to prove to us the toxicity of wine and the deplorable effects it has on the human body and mind.

Yet, can you imagine a good meal that is not accompanied by a well chosen, honest, good quality wine? In France, in the gastronomical pages even of certain medical journals, we read complicated recipes every month for delicacies cooked in fine wines such as

4

Bourgeuil or Chinon, which are also recommended to be served with the meal.

All these antiwine campaigns do not however obscure the fact, for instance, that the water we use for drinking purposes is becoming more and more polluted. Or that the regular use of toxic products such as narcotics, hallucinogenic drugs and tranquilizers is becoming daily more commonplace. And it almost seems as if no one is concerned. But, when it comes to wine ...

We have read quite recently in the medical press about some experiments conducted by doctors in Hungary, indicating a relationship between the frequency of kidney stones and the quality of drinking water: high calcium content in water causes the formation of stones. And research still in progress tends to confirm this hypothesis. Professor Crawford, of St. George's Hospital in London, has also proven that the quality of tap water may be a factor in precipitating heart attacks. He has observed a higher percentage of coronary lesions in London, where the water is hard, than in Glasgow, where the water is softer.

This is why, following the steps of many excellent writers to whom we shall frequently refer, I decided to take up the challenge to defend the divine beverage which warms the hearts of men; for as Ecclesiastes put it: *vinum et musica laetificat cor* (wine and music make the heart happy).

There is one condition, however, that must be fulfilled if our plea is to win its case. And that concerns the quality of the wine—the very crux of the problem.

In fact it is easy enough to demonstrate the toxicity of the fermented juice of the vine if the vegetal element, which plays the most important part in the making of wine, is almost absent in the wine itself or, rather, in a substitute that is wrongly labeled wine. Bad wine, according to P. Delore, is "the wine which has been tampered with, which has been fraudulently treated in the making, especially by the addition of sodium metasulfide, which produces a dead wine, the ferments of which have been destroyed."

Among some writers, this statement would be seen as inexact. They would point out that the "must" (unfermented grape juice) SO_2 acts on the live yeasts and the fermentation process does take place naturally. Indeed, in the case of wines containing residual sugar, we can speak of *biologically* stabilized wines.

But we should also remember the quip attributed to a wine producer who on his deathbed told his children, ". . . and remember, my children, that wine can also be made from grapes."

Is it necessary to stress that a good quality wine, taken in reasonable dosage—such as those which I shall indicate in the following pages—never has harmful effects on the body, unlike many of the classic medications? Each of us can remember experiencing a bad hangover after drinking too much wine, either red or white, from a bottle treacherously labeled *appellation contrôlée,* the term which appears on the label of fine French wines, signifying origin and the right to the name it bears, guaranteed according to French law. These wines were of course nothing but adulterated products, the work of clever chemists. It is such experiences that educate the palate, so that one will thereafter be able to distinguish a good wine from a bad one, and to refrain from drinking any liquid which has been falsified, and is therefore in essence toxic.

This type of fraud has, of course, always been around. In the eighteenth century the magazine *La Gazette de Santé* reminded its readers that "if the wine destined for our use were always pure and natural, free of mixture and drunk in moderation, we believe that, far from shortening the lifespan, it would be capable of lengthening it. But such is the misfortune of those who indulge in such a drink, especially in the capital, that an excess of it becomes deadly and even its moderate use is noxious."

One could not say it better today.

Apart from the blending and adulteration which alter the original purity of the liquid, one should also be aware that there are sick wines. Like any living organism, the juice from the vine is not exempt from diseases, such as *la casse,* a chemical disease of wines resulting from excess iron. This disease is due to a polyphenoloxydase secreted by the *Botrytis Cinerea.* It is due to failure to take precautions against contamination during the wine-making process. To obtain a good quality wine, for instance, the wine maker must take care to protect his vine stocks from the weed-killing hormones, since the vine is highly susceptible and reacts to the slightest dosage, no matter which hormone is used.

Moreover, as I have already suggested, it is not only the quality of the wine which is in question, but the quantity as well. I stress this factor in the following pages, especially since they are meant for people suffering from various afflictions. Everything is a question of moderation. As Pascal said: "Too much or too little wine: don't give him any and he can't find the truth; give him too much and it is the same."

Since our purpose, perhaps a bit rash but nonetheless well-meant, is to advocate wine both as a nutriment and especially as a remedy to support other medical treatments and therapies, we will present it in this book as a substance gifted with definite therapeutic qualities. But as is the case with any medicine, we shall determine the dosage according to the malady, the individual, and the age of the patient.

The reader should be reminded that any therapeutic agent involves two different and potentially opposite actions, according to the quantity that is absorbed. The fundamental experiments upon which Samuel Hahnemann, the genial founder of homeopathy, based his research have convinced us of this. Homeopathy demonstrates that "the best is the enemy of the good." A small amount of coffee stimulates; too much of it causes, among other discomforts, dizziness, palpitations, and insomnia. A medicine properly proportioned is beneficial; an overdose of it can lead to poisoning and may even be fatal. We see today a great many examples of the results of intemperate use of the latest synthetic products, which bear the guarantee of clinical testing as well as the stamp of government approval.

Everything is a question of moderation, the use of wine like everything else.

We remain convinced that if we respect these two imperatives—quality and quantity—wine, far from being the noxious drink it has been so complacently called, remains the best and healthiest of drinks for the human being, as Louis Pasteur proclaimed.

This work, which has no scientific pretensions, is

intended for everyone, but most especially for people who are ill, and for the vast number of those who must, or believe they must, follow a strict diet. I address myself to them as a doctor and I base my arguments on the oenological works of researchers whose names I will quote throughout these pages, and on the authority of the defenders of the fermented juice of the vine.

In doing so I hope to teach these patients a new *joie de vivre*—in itself something positive in a period where most things conspire to make life more and more difficult. I want even the man or woman on a diet to be able to sit down once again at a meal with pleasure. The strictly planned diet should be lightened by reasonable amounts of an honest wine, correctly chosen according to each clinical case. First Pasteur, and then Madame Randouin, have insisted on the fact that wine represents a complete nutritive element thanks to its vitamin content and its many other components, which we shall mention in the first half of this book. We are mindful that too strict a diet can in fact deprive the digestive system of its natural function, the secretion of ferments essential to good digestion and proper assimilation. This can lead, even in mild cases, to neurasthenia and depression. Indeed, how many suicides and how many nervous breakdowns are due to poorly planned diets! In a chapter of this book we shall study the highly beneficial action of wine on the digestive system and on the mechanism of digestion. I recall a patient I examined at the very beginning of my career who died prematurely because he followed to an extreme the dietary instructions of a doctor who was far too dogmatic and absolute. The patient got to the point where he could not tolerate any food, and he simply died of hunger. His financial situation would have allowed him to satisfy any of his whims, had he had any. Analysts and psychiatrists will probably see this case as an example of masochism. That it most certainly was. But if this poor patient had been willing to restrict his abuse of mineral water and to complete his daily ration of liquid with a good wine, carefully selected, he would have seen life differently and would not have condemned himself to the painful end which was his.

"Measure above all," said the poet. This expression was never better applied than here. But, enough talking. Will you join me at table?

PART ONE

WINE IN NATURE

"De tonne en verre, le voilà le joli verre."
(Old Bacchic song)

Chapter 1

ANATOMY OF WINE

Winelovers are in the habit of attributing to wine qualities which are more usually applied to a human being. They talk about its body, muscle, and nerve, not to speak, like Baudelaire, of its soul.

These terms are metaphors to enable us to consider the juice of the vine as a living being, and thus to study its anatomy in the sense of its proper structure.

THE COLOR OF WINE

Before going any further into the main part of our subject matter, we should say a word about the different colors which allow us to distinguish between wines.

White wines owe their color to the processing of white vine stocks, like the Blanc de Blanc, or gray vine stocks, like the Pinot gris, or red wine stocks according to a process unique to the Champagne region.

Red wines come from the crushing of red grapes, whose "must" is then fermented with or without the grape pips.

As for *rosé wines,* their color is due to a special processing, which is the same as that for the "gray" wines, or wines of the Côtes de Toul, but applied to grapes that do not come from gray vine stocks.

13

Yellow wines, such as the Arbois, the Château-Chalon, the Côtes du Jura, come from the *savagnin,* a special vine stock. Such wines are kept in wooden casks for at least six years. And let us not forget the *vins de paille,* or *straw wines,* so called because the fresh crops of grapes are spread upon straw to dry for a period of time before they are pressed.

NOTES ON THE GEOLOGICAL COMPOSITION
OF THE SOIL OF ORIGIN

Like man, for whose exclusive use it is intended, the vine is closely rooted to the soil on which it grows, and from which it will borrow a great many elements which make up its juice—I almost wrote its blood, since we are here talking about anatomy.

These elements, as we shall see later on, will be absorbed by man as he drinks the wine when it has reached full maturity. They will then play a double role: first as a food and eventually as a medicine.

We should not forget that analysis shows that this vegetable blood contains about 250 chemical substances, most of which are borrowed from the soil. We shall study the main ones in a different chapter.

We do not intend here an in-depth geological study of all the soils on which vines grow. That would be far beyond the scope of this modest study, which will remain above all a practical guide to the medicinal properties of different wines.

But we shall briefly describe the composition of the soil of some of the best known winegrowing areas in France. And we will do this in order to demonstrate that when you drink a wine you drink not a simple liquid, whose color and taste vary according to region, year and type of vineyard, but a noble beverage, a complete food, and a well tolerated medicine which carries, among other things, some perfectly assimilable mineral elements borrowed from the soil on which it grew under the warm rays of the sun.

Before proceeding to a brief summary of the varieties of wines in France, we should recall that the current vine stocks come from the root *vitis vinifera caucasia* (Caucasian wine vine), whose name is an indication of its origin. First the Greeks, and then the Romans, in their conquests transplanted the vine successively around the entire Mediterranean basin.

In France today, the vine is cultivated south of a line which extends from Nantes through Rheims to Strasbourg. French vineyards represent an area of about 3,500,000 acres, of which 3,200,000 are productive.

Before going into more detail, we should remember that 90 percent of French viticultural soils are calcareous (high in limestone). Some areas, such as the Champagne or Cognac regions, have an exceptionally high proportion of limestone. This means that they must be planted with grafting-stands capable of resisting lime carbonate, for a vine not resistant to lime will fall victim to chlorosis, and in order to give new vitality to such stock it would be necessary to add an iron salt which would go through into the juice itself. Here again, the comparison with human physiology is evident!

THE BORDEAUX REGION

To begin with, the vineyards of the Bordeaux region—

one of the oldest of French wine regions—grow on a terrain consisting primarily of limestone and silica. While the soil of the Graves subregion, actually the most favorable for winegrowing, is made of pure sand containing particles of iron, the hillsides are made of clay rich in aluminum silicates. The soil of the Bordeaux region also contains potassium and its humus holds tannin. Later on we shall see the use and medicinal role of these elements in human metabolism.

THE BURGUNDY REGION

The vineyards of Burgundy offer a whole range of different wines.

From north to south we find a succession of different winegrowing districts: Côtes de Dijon; Côtes de Nuit with its Chambertins, its Gevrey, its Clos-Vougeot; Côte de Beaune, whose soil is made of limestone mixed with white ferruginous marls; the Macon region which includes the area of Juliens, Fleuries and Chiroubles, rich in silica; the Beaujolais area where the soil is granite; and its immediate neighbor, the region of Chablis, whose wines are grown on a soil which originates in *killerdjian* marls rich in pebbles and containing a high proportion of silica.

THE RHÔNE REGION

A little lower on the pleasant hills along the two banks of the Rhône between Vienne and Avignon, the vineyards produce a wine called Côtes du Rhône. The vines grow on a terrain composed of such hard and dense pebbles that to plow it the farmer has to change his iron plowshare every three hours. From this soil the wine derives its strength, and thanks to the progress in current wine-making it has lost its original heaviness and thickness.

THE JURA AREA

To the southeast of Burgundy, the Jura, with its ground of clay and limestone, offers us its wines of Salins, sprung from a Pinot Blanc; those of Arbois, dry and fruity; and its yellow wines with their strong aroma. All of them contain minerals essential to man. And since we are talking here about the Jura, let us remember that Louis Pasteur, one of the strongest believers in the juice of the vine, was born here.

PROVENCE

To finish with the winegrowing areas of southeastern France, we must mention blue-skied Provence. Its soil is considered calcareous because of its geological composition and because of the important role played by the sun, the crystal-clear light, and the atmosphere of the region. Its vineyards produce light, dry and fragrant wines, a fitting accompaniment to seafood which is full of natural iodine.

THE SOUTHWEST

Following the course of the sun, we come to the plains and hills region of Languedoc-Roussillon. This is made up of low-resistance terrain, marl, grit, sand, and round pebbles, with vineyards covering most of the tillable soil.

Its geological composition lends itself admirably to vine growing, and produces pleasant *vin ordinaire* for daily domestic consumption.

Mention should also be made of some pleasing and proud, fiery and velvety wines from the Roussillon area, including such natural products as Banyuls, Maury, Muscats de Frontignan, and Rivesaltes. In any wine cellar these wines can play the role of a Port wine.

THE LOIRE REGION

If we go now to the Val de Loire, between Blois and the mouth of this royal river, we find the Touraine, the land of Rabelais, Ronsard and Balzac, where the wealth and the variety of white and red wines would make any honest man happy.

The soil of the chalky slopes and of the rocky terrain is usually supported by tufa, which is a mica or sand chalk. In the Saumur region, on the contrary, there is a predominance of clay and limestone and sometimes of silica. The Vouvray vineyard grows on a soil rich in chalk and it produces young, fresh, dry and semidry wines, which according to a local motto "warm up hearts."

Bourgueil and Chinon on the other hand offer the palate the pleasure of fruity, flowery wines. And closer to its spring, the river flows between hills where the vine stocks of Sauvignon grow. These yield Sancerre and Pouilly, clear, dry and lively wines, the true wines for thirsty days.

THE CHAMPAGNE AREA

Let us leave these pleasant regions to stop for a minute

in the heart of the Champagne area which has given man this unique beverage which symbolizes *joie de vivre*. If the Chardonnet vine stock gives the wine its freshness and smoothness, the Pinot noir and the Pinot Meunier give it body and bone structure. From this happy combination the Dom Pérignon, which stimulates the affective centers, is born. Didn't a poet write that Champagne is "the brilliant image of the French people"? To the Marquise de Pompadour, this wine was to be valued for making women even more beautiful, and God knows that the Marquise was knowledgeable about that. We will expand on these qualities later on.

ALSACE

A little further to the east, the Alsace region gives us dry white wines, so transparent that they let the light right through. Their acidity, expressed in terms of sulfuric acid content, is between 3 and 5 grams (about 1 teaspoon).

It is obvious that if we wanted to mention here all the varieties of wines that one can taste and enjoy on a journey through France, we would need several volumes. We can only briefly mention wines such as the Costières from the Gard, the Minervois, the Corbières and the Cahors wines, all symbols of the pleasure of drinking and living. Other less known wines, but as highly recommended for their taste as well as for their therapeutic virtues, should be noted; such as the Lorraine wines, as fresh as the winds and the water from the Moselle river; and the Savoie wines, whether white, rosé or red, which are dry, rough and straightforward. But to go into more detail would take us beyond the scope of this work.

Chapter 2

THE CHEMISTRY OF WINE

Since from the very first pages of this work we have, perhaps arbitrarily, likened the juice of the vine to a living organism, and have studied its anatomy with its different attributes according to the soil on which it grew, it would now be appropriate to analyze the chemical composition of this vegetable blood.

Before going into more detail, and to give an idea of its nutritive content, we should note that 1 liter (approximately 1 quart) of wine contains 800 to 900 grams (80 to 90 percent) water, 20 to 30 grams (2 to 3 percent) of glucose and fructose, 5 to 10 grams (.5 to 1 percent) of glycerine, 6 to 12 grams (.6 to 1.2 percent) of various organic acids, a few grams of potassium, calcium, and iron and 60 to 100 grams (6 to 10 percent) of ethyl alcohol. We also find in suspension some tannin, peptic matter, and residual yeasts, mycoderms, saccharomyces, and deacidifying malo-lactic bacteria.

Analysis of the composition of wine will allow us better to understand the role that wine is capable of playing in certain pathological conditions, and the therapeutic help it can bring to both the sick and the healthy.

Let us first recall the definition jurists have given of wine: "the product of the fermentation of grapes or of fresh grape juice." Wine is a natural product, a combustion element as well as a building element for the human cell.

WINE AND THE HIPPOCRATIC ELEMENTS

Wine comes from living cells which are the very berries of the vine. Their juice is later on transformed, by the operation of other living cells such as yeast or lactic bacteria.

This natural product, the must, includes about 250 chemical agents, and we shall study the main ones later on. It is the end result of a slow maturing process which takes place in the shade of cool cellars. It can be considered, in a way, as a true synthesis of the four main elements which, according to the traditional Hippocratic principles, constitute the basics of life, that is to say: earth, air, fire and water. In wine these elements are represented, in more scientific terms, apart from the liquid element, by the mineral salts and the organic substances of which it is composed.

The "fire" element of the wine is symbolically represented by its alcohol content. We will mention this again in a later chapter, from the therapeutic point of view. In chemical terms, apart from ethyl alcohol, the fermented grape juice contains glycerine, an alcohol derivative, in proportions varying from 3.50 to 15 grams (about 1 teaspoon to 1 tablespoon) per liter. This agent normally exists in the intestine produced by the double decomposition of fats, and it joins with phosphates to make assimilable glycerophosphates.

The group of elements which enter into the composition of the must is practically the same for all wines.

Such differences as do exist are due to the fact that the proportion of each element is variable according to the origin of the stock and the nature of the soil on which the vine grew. I mentioned this briefly in the geological outline of the preceding chapter. This is why, to give but one example, the full-bodied wines like Burgundy or Châteauneuf-du-Pape, which are drunk preferably only after some years of aging in the bottle, are richer in alcohol and in minerals than lighter wines which are to be drunk young and are poorer in these elements. Their therapeutic indications will also be different.

As for the presence of water in grape juice, it gives to wine, because of the presence of alcohol, a density very close to its own. This represents a guarantee of isotonicity. Moreover, the water, which is drawn through the roots of the vine from cultivated soil and subsoil, is a "mineralized" water. It is the indispensable vehicle which carries the other elements which contribute to the originality and the richness of each wine.

Obviously the water content can be variable for each wine, depending on the nature of the soil and the amount of precipitation. And it is to be hoped that the grower will respect the quantity given to him by the fruit itself, without adding a supplement. However, since wine is sold today according to alcohol percentage, addition of water would not make sense.

THE MINERAL ELEMENTS

Among the "Hippocratic" substances of the "earth" type that chemical analysis can detect in grape juice, we find, in the first place, the mineral elements which are easily isolated by the calcination of the organic substances. They exist as salts or oxides.

The mineral salts which are found in wine in a scattered state, thanks to the presence of microorganisms which oxidize them, are indispensable to the human body. They can be assimilated best as organic salts, that is to say combined with animal or vegetable substances. In wine, the mineral salts are found incorporated in their assimilable form in a state of ionization. Thus, according to Dr. Dougnac, they are capable of starting or accelerating a whole series of secondary organic reactions. Among the mineral anions, phosphorus, in its phosphate form, is particularly bountiful in red wine where it can reach levels of 0.08 to 0.50. An element essential for bone tissues, phosphorus combined with calcium plays a major role in maintaining the acid basic balance of the blood. It accelerates the metabolism of nitrogenous exchanges and it acts upon fats and sugars, which it transforms, releasing the necessary energy for muscular contraction.

Chlorine and sodium, which we shall discuss later, are found in grape juice from seashore areas. Sulfur is present in almost all wines as sulfate. Thanks to this element, the liver can play its role of detoxification and protection against microbic and organic toxins.

Among the other elements we can count iodine, silica, boron, and bromine. We should also mention the presence of fluorine, whose action on soft tissues is now known; and of magnesium, calcium, sodium, and potassium. Each of these elements deserves a short comment on its properties.

Magnesium

Magnesium, a major element which is present in the soft tissues, particularly in the cells of the brain and spine, as well as in the bones, is one of the fundamental components of living matter. As the conveyor of phosphorus, it is essential to the synthesis of the organophosphorus compounds and plays an important role in building bones through its action on calcium fixation. It is necessary for the reduction of sugars, and plays a part in muscular contraction. And its action on the white blood cells helps them defend the body against infection.

Calcium

We know that calcium is assimilated by bone tissue to insure the growth of the skeleton, and to preserve the health of the bone structure in later life. Another property of calcium is its intervention in activating pancreatic juices, which allows animal and vegetable nitrogenous matter to be transformed into peptones. Calcium also plays a part in blood coagulation, since the constituents in blood responsible for the formation of thrombin can only act in the presence of ionized calcium.

Sodium

Sodium insures the molecular equilibrium between liquids inside the cells and outside them. Moreover the sodium ions play an important part in nervous and muscular fibers. If the sodium content falls drastically, the neuromuscular response is disturbed and can be blocked.

Potassium

This alkaline metal, an element essential to life, promotes the normal function of the nerve cell, particularly the automatic action of the heart. When we come to deal with therapy, we will stress the role that wine can play for the cardiac patient.

It should also be noted that all these chemical elements act in synergy, and complement each other in their actions. Therefore wine, as a solution balanced in monovalent and bivalent mineral salts contained in physiological dosage, constitutes a marvelous natural vehicle—and a most pleasant one to the taste—for supportive therapy during illness, uniquely adapted as it is to the essential needs of the human being.

Iron

Special mention must be made of iron, whose presence in wine constitutes a real medicine. The fermented grape juice contains an average of 4.4 mg of iron per liter, and in Bordeaux or Burgundy wines this level is as high as 6 mg. It is not surprising therefore that this vegetable blood with its warm red color has always been recommended for anemics, and for people recovering from serious illness.

THE ORGANIC ELEMENTS

Along with the mineral elements, of which we have noted the most important ones, wine contains many organic substances which come directly from the grape itself.

Monosaccharides

Let us first mention, because of the importance of their presence in wine, the carbohydrates, also called monosaccharides or inverted sugars, and present in wine as glucose and fructose. The amount in which they are present gives wine its dry or mellow taste. This natural sugar is accumulated in the liver where it is stored until the body feels a need for it.

Red and dry white wines generally contain less than 2 grams (.2 percent) of residual sugars (arabinose, xylose) per liter. The so-called sweet or mellow wines retain some sugar thanks to the sulfur dioxide which is added to prevent a later refermentation.

Peptides

The peptides come from the insoluble part of the grape and are more numerous in red wines than in white wines. They are nitrogenous substances which include polypeptides, proteins, and amino acids. Among the latter are found lysin, arginine, histamine, glutaminic and aspartic acids whose energizing action is now known. Ordinary wines are not very rich in these substances, whereas good quality wines contain a fairly high proportion of them.

All of these natural substances release the nitrogen

27

every organism needs for its metabolic processes.

Phenols

Wine also contains phenolic compounds—phenols and flavones—which give wine certain antiseptic properties, and also the colored pigments that distinguish red and white wines.

From the medical and dietetic point of view, the only one we are here concerned with, we should remember that wines have the ability, thanks to the phenols they contain, to destroy the pathogenic bacteria which can contaminate drinking water or food eaten raw. For a long time red wine has also been used externally for the treatment of infected wounds and ulcerations. And experiments have also shown that the polyphenols contained in wine confer protection on laboratory animals fed a high-cholesterol diet. Organic acids are also found in large quantities in wine. The more important ones among them are tartaric acid, whose normal level is between 2 and 5 grams (from .2 to .5 percent) per liter, succinic, malic, acetic and citric acids. And we should not forget lactic acid, which totally replaces the malic acid after the malolactic fermentation.

All of these contribute to the physiological action of the chyme of the stomach by increasing the bile and pancreatic secretions, and therefore accelerating the digestion of fatty substances.

TANNOID PRODUCTS

The tannoid products incorporated in wine, through the medium of the oak cask or the presence of the oenotannins found in a natural state in the stems, skins, and pips, have antitoxic effects on some other wine components, such as ethanol and methanol, by helping to lessen their irritative action on the nervous system.

We know that white wines, which are more intoxicating and stimulating than red wines, contain little tannin. The oenotannins, which will be treated in more detail in the chapter on the physiology of wine, and which have been well studied by Dr. Dougnac, contain iron and therefore act as a tonic for the blood. They also act as an antidote to most of the alkaloids. And they are further believed to encourage growth, and to have beneficial effects in the treatment of tuberculosis.

ENZYMES

As for the enzymes, the soluble organic agents whose function it is to accelerate all the chemical and biological reactions, they come either from the fruit itself, or from the microorganisms which develop in it during fermentation. They are found in very large numbers in wine—catalases, oxydases, invertases, proteases, pectases—each contributing to make wine a whole, truly living food.

To complete this chapter, we wish to go back once more to the main objection many dietitians have to wine—that is to say, its alcoholic content.

It is a fact that alcohol represents about one-tenth of

the volume of wine, and that it is one of its essential elements. It is admitted that an excess of alcohol in the blood may cause functional problems and more or less severe organic lesions. But, as always in pharmacology, everything is a matter of dosage. Even among the strictest believers in pure foods, it is recognized that in normally fed subjects, a dose of 2 grams of alcohol per kilo of body weight can constitute a beneficial-reserve nutriment without producing metabolic modifications.

Professor Gounelle, who is an authority on the subject, claims that "the dose of 100 milliliters [about ½ cup] is the maximum daily allowance of alcohol; it corresponds to 1 liter [about 1 quart] of 10% wine, excluding all other alcoholic beverage."

Chapter 3

WINE AND VITAMINS

On several occasions in the preceding chapter we have insisted upon the fact that wine constitutes a living organism and we have seen why. But the factor which confers on it an even more important nutritive value is the presence of a number of natural vitamins—not synthetic ones such as those which so many people have a tendency to consume these days. And it is not unreasonable to predict that future analyses of wine will identify other useful vitamins.

So let us devote some brief attention to them.

At the end of the last century, researchers succeeded in isolating in foods and drinks certain elements found to play a central role in alimentary balance, and whose deficiency could cause ill-health. The oldest and best known example was the discovery that scurvy (scorbutus), a condition that affected sailors on long sea voyages deprived of fresh food, could be cured dramatically by drinking fresh lemon juice, which contains a high level of vitamin C.

Although specialists do not agree on the exact definition of the term "vitamin," one fact is evident: vitamins constitute an indispensable contribution to biological balance, and a deficiency of any one of them can cause troubles. Some of these conditions are now known and labeled, but others involve a variety of symptoms which do not constitute a known or clinically described disease, and are generally grouped as "deficiency diseases."

There are in particular certain periods of our lives, including certain illnesses, when the human body needs a *supplement* of vitamins—during puberty or pregnancy for instance, or while breast feeding, during or after a period of overwork, in old age, or while suffering acute or chronic debilitating diseases, such as tuberculosis or rheumatism. We should not forget either that modern living, with its repeated emotional excesses and its continual stress, creates in man a constant need for vitamins to replace his constant loss of energy.

This means that these elements are a vital necessity, especially when they can be provided through natural substances—which are those most easily assimilated by the body—such as are found in the chemical analysis of good quality wine.

OENOTANNINS

Among the chemical products in solution in wine already mentioned is the tannic matter which forms the coloring elements of wine.

In the next chapter we shall treat the physiological role of tannins on digestion, but for the time being we will deal with them only as a source of vitamins.

The recent work of Lavollay and Sevestre has shown an association between these tannic substances, or to use the current expression "oenotannins," and factor P. White and black grapes are the fruit in which the activity of factor P is at its highest and its action continues in wine even after alcoholic fermentation. This factor P is one of the two antiscorbutic vitamins. It acts in relation to the ascorbic acid present in vitamin C (which we shall discuss later on). A deficiency of P in the organism causes a reduction in capillary resilience, and modifications of the threshold of muscular and nervous excitation, as some experiments by these two scientists on guinea pigs have shown.

Consequently wine, especially red wine, might under medical supervision help relieve purpura, an affliction which shows itself in reddish spots on the skin due to the breaking of the small subcutaneous blood vessels.

According to Parrot the tannic substances rich in vitamin P, in liaison with ascorbic acid, also act as a factor in the reserve system of the body.

Therefore, to conclude this brief study of vitamin P, the presence of oenotannins in wine makes this beverage one of the most pleasurable ways of insuring that the body is able to absorb substances which are indispensable for its functioning and reserve system, but which are often destroyed in cooked foods.

OTHER VITAMINS

When we speak about vitamins in wine we are speaking about essentially water-soluble vitamins. We are of course considering only those which have been recognized, and whose dosages have been determined.

Vitamin C

Vitamin C, an antiscorbutic, plays an important role in

most metabolic processes, particularly in the one concerned with the use of glucoses. It allows the synthesis of
endocrinous substances secreted by the suprarenal cortex.
Further, the presence of ascorbic acid in the upper part
of the intestine is necessary for the assimilation of iron,
which will eventually fix itself in the red blood cells. It
also acts indirectly but actively on the formation of
hemoglobin, the colored pigment of the red blood cell
which is responsible for carrying oxygen towards the
tissues.

Several medical writers have recently warned of the
dangers of the present fashion for synthetic vitamin
therapy. They point out that although the dosages used
in such therapy are indeed sufficient to avoid deficiencies, they in fact often represent at least *three times*
the amount really needed by the human body (estimated
at 75 mg per day). Any excess, often taken by a patient
on his own initiative and without medical advice, disturbs
the normal balance which is necessary between hormones, enzymes, and other vitamins.

Wine, on the other hand, as a natural food, carries its
vitamins in sufficient amounts without any danger of
disturbing the system's normal vitamin balance.

B Vitamins

What has been said about vitamin C could equally
apply to the other vitamins found in wine, and particularly to the B vitamins, which constitute a group of
substances of common origin in the form of yeasts. The
general properties of this group of vitamins—each of
which we shall consider in more detail later on—act, first

of all, on the nervous system. They also help in the regulation of blood-sugar level, act on intracellular oxidation and on endocrine functions, and on muscle tone.

Chemical analysis of wine has allowed us to isolate these vitamins and to establish their dosage.

Vitamin B_1 or thiamine accumulates in the pulp of the grape and is found especially in red wines. It represents an important element in the nutrition of the nervous system, since its pathological deficiency causes the disease known as beriberi, whose symptoms are cardio-vascular troubles, edema, leading to multiple neuritis with paralysis.

Vitamin B_3, also called vitamin PP, is a nicotinamide. It is found in both red and white wines in the proportion 800 to 1900 micrograms (a microgram is one-millionth of a gram) per liter. According to Lavollay and Sevestre, it acts on asthenic conditions with low blood pressure and serves as a reserve element for vitamin C. Moreover it constitutes, as indicated by its initials, a preventative factor against pellagra (PP), a disease characterized by skin lesions and digestive troubles. It also plays a part in oxidation-reduction phenomena.

Riboflavin, another vitamin of the B group, is also abundant in red wine. At a level of 100 to 200 grams (10 to 20 percent) per liter, it has a nutritive value and intervenes in the metabolism of glucides and protides, iron, vitamins A, B_1 and PP, as well as the corticosuprarenal hormones. It also acts on the poorly vascularized tissues such as the crystalline tissue of the eye and the cornea. A deficiency of riboflavin leads to ocular troubles whose symptoms are photophobia, burning of the eyelids, visual fatigue, and production of tears.

As for vitamin B_5 or pantothenic acid, it exists in both types of wine in fairly good quantities. Any deficiency seems to lead to some degree of malnutrition of the body and to cause cutaneous, respiratory and nervous problems.

Finally, apart from vitamin B_6 or pyridoxine, which intercedes at different stages of the metabolic process and is found in both red and white wines, we should also mention the presence of vitamin B_{12} or cyano-cobalamine, whose action on the formation of red cells is well known. It is an important antianemic factor, and it is interesting to note that this vitamin protects the experimental guinea pig against the fatty degeneration caused by carbon tetrachloride. Given in massive doses it represents a therapeutic element used in the treatment of cirrhosis of the liver. We can therefore deduce that when used in normal doses it is capable, to a certain extent, of preventing liver damage.

We can conclude this short chapter by saying that it is certainly more pleasant to absorb natural vitamins in a good glass of honest and pure wine than to take them as pills!

Chapter 4

THE PHYSIOLOGY OF WINE

Just as, if we were attempting to understand the physical behavior of man, we would study his anatomy, bio-chemistry and physiology, so, up to now, we have been doing with wine. Having looked at wine's "anatomy," and its chemical and vitamin composition, we must now turn to its "physiological" aspect. We shall review the nature of the organic functions upon which wine acts.

Before going into detail, we can say that wine is in general a medicine, able to compensate with its live fer-ments for various deficiencies in the human body.

At the physical level, it warms us up and calms thirst and hunger. On the psychic level, it increases cerebral activity in a euphoric way. We will come to write about this a little further on.

Many writers, some of whom are well meaning, have published learned works on what they call the "physio-pathological effects of wine" and we cannot deny that these writers have only expressed the sad truth.

It is a known fact, and no one will deny it, that wine, like nearly all the food products put out on the market for our daily consumption, is subjected to artificial chemical adulteration. This is done by those who sell it to the public in the name of what our kind technocrats, who are really frustrated humorists, have labeled "pro-ductivity."

We can only assume that behind this beautiful euphemism is hidden the desire, quite natural no doubt on the part of the producer and even more of the dis- tributor, to increase profit margins. But although the French government, which has so often been attacked about this, has run several campaigns against alcoholism, it is still too lenient with wine falsification. For it is the use of chemical additives that augments alcohol content and turns wine into a toxic product which is no longer a food, much less a medicine.

For many who have studied this question, particularly Dr. Dougnac, "grape juice cannot be considered a simple alcoholic dilution."

Wine is rich in all the chemical elements that are found in the analysis of the solar spectrum. We stressed this fact in the preceding chapter. Certain elements of wine have a definite antialcoholic action. Moreover the pH of wine, that is the coefficient which characterizes its degree of acidity or base, varies from 2.7 to 3.2. This natural acidity, particularly in white wine, encourages salivary secretion. This pH, physiologically speaking, is close to that of gastric juice. When a wine causes heartburn, it may be because it has been falsified or, if natural, made from insufficiently mature grapes.

But before we talk about its action on the reflex behavior of the stomach, we should first mention that wine, whether taken as a food or as a therapeutic agent, affects the upper digestive tract: mouth, tongue, palate, esophagus. By direct contact with the mucous mem-branes of these organs, wine sets off a series of biophysiological reactions affecting all of the digestive system.

ACTION ON THE DIGESTIVE TRACT

We know that the sensations of smell and taste, born respectively in the nasal fossa and in the mouth, are activated by a good quality wine. These sensory impressions act in turn on the nervous input to the upper brain centers. This explains the euphoric feeling experienced after first seeing, then drinking, moderately and intelligently, a good quality wine. It is as the wine is warmed inside the mouth that the subtle tastes and aromas are released which give each wine its characteristic flavor.

Moreover, the sensory reflex, like that of Pavlov's dogs, is first aroused by the color and the smell of the selected wine, which excites the secretion of saliva, before even the wine reaches the mouth and encourages the partial digestion of farinaceous or sweet food.

Once in the stomach, wine, thanks to its alcohol content and its vitamins, augments the secretions of the gastric wall and therefore also the level of hydrochloric acid. Experiments have shown that the ingestion of 60 to 100 grams (2.2 to 3.4 ounces) of wine facilitates the secretion of 120 grams (4 ounces) of a liquid containing about one gram of free hydrochloric acid within half an hour.

According to Dr. Marchal, the drinking of wine also causes an influx of white blood cells, which are a source of oxidizing ferments. The yeasts in the wine act on the food while it is in the process of being digested.

Didn't St. Paul say one day to one of his followers who

was complaining of digestive troubles: "Drink no longer water, but use a little wine for thy stomach's sake and thine often infirmities."

Following its course down the digestive tract, wine goes next through the duodenum and the small intestine. The glycerine that is normally present in wine, added to that which is normally found in this part of the digestive tract, combines with the natural phosphates in wine to form glycerol-phosphates, which are stored as body reserves to be used as the need arises.

According to Ferrand and his collaborators, this glycerine enters the liver through the lymphatic vessels, where it then aids in breaking down fats and protides. In addition, it also encourages the secretion of pancreatic lipases, thus helping in the hydrolysis of fats.

The presence of tannin, which we have already mentioned in another chapter and which is found especially in red wines, acts on the smooth fibers of the muscles of the digestive tract and consequently promotes peristalsis.

This physiological contraction of the smooth musculature of the digestive tract also facilitates the action of the gall bladder, and the common bile duct which carries the bile into the intestine during the digestive process. Wine acts, then, at this level by increasing the secretion of bile, thus helping alimentary metabolic action. This phenomenon was observed by Loeper, who ascertained that ingestion of 20 ml (.6 ounces) of wine enabled him to gather about 190 grams (6½ ounces) of bile in a duodenal tube.

According to Dr. Dougnac, a reasonable amount of wine is beneficial to the liver too, as long as it is functioning well. Wine increases the production of white blood cells inside the liver, a phenomenon similar to that noted by Dr. Marchal in regard to the stomach.

In this respect wine has a bactericide action which has always been known. Surgeons of old used it lavishly to sterilize infected wounds. In our more scientific times we continue to show interest in this property of wine, and researchers have experimentally established that one cubic centimeter of white wine kills 99 percent of the typhus bacilli, cholera microbes and coliform bacilli contained in one ml of culture medium. This antibiotic action is due to the alcohol content of wine, its acids, and its tannin content and ethers.

We can conclude that good quality wine acts favorably at all stages in the digestive system provided, one more time, that its consumption remains within reasonable limits.

ACTION ON THE NERVOUS SYSTEM

As for the influence of wine on the whole nervous system, this is governed, particularly in the sphere of the central nervous system, by the inherent need of every normal human being to use a stimulant. Instead of turning to toxic and illegal products for a euphoriant, why not more simply turn to good wine, a natural and healthy substance? Moreover, the natural phosphorus in wine, indispensable to the nutrition of the brain cells, is certainly better tolerated by the body than that taken in a synthetic form.

ACTION ON THE URINARY SYSTEM

It is hardly necessary to stress the influence that wine, and particularly white wine, has on the urinary system. It acts on the renal parenchyma as a diuretic. According to Professor Carles, the noticeable increase in the volume of urine is the result of the acidity of white wines and their rich tartrate content.

ACTION ON THE CARDIOVASCULAR SYSTEM

To complete this brief summary of the action of wine on the main systems of the body, we must say a word about the effects of wine on the cardiovascular system. Though no cardiac patient should drink alcohol without medical advice, Professor Laubry and Dr. Lemant once demonstrated experimentally that an intravenous injection of an alcohol solution and physiological salt solution at 33 percent caused no increase in blood pressure. Similarly, the drinking of two glasses of 12% red wine on an empty stomach at a one half-hour interval caused only very minor cardiac and vascular modifications. In all cases and in all the subjects who volunteered themselves for these experiments, electrocardiographs showed no changes.

According to Fiessinger, arteriosclerosis and the tendency to atherosis, especially the form which affects the cerebral arteries, are more frequent in water drinkers. Finally, Dr. Encausse permits the athlete, who regularly exercises his muscles and his cardiovascular system, a daily dosage of three-quarters of a liter of wine, either a Bordeaux or a light Beaujolais—when he is not in intensive training, at least. On the other hand, the athlete should not drink white wine, which has the reputation of taking away energy.

In conclusion we can say that good quality wine is at the same time a body-building food, a dietary complement, a supporting therapy, a chemical conveyor of natural products, and a psychic tonic. I repeat, with all due respect to its detractors, that all these qualities are endowments of fermented grape juice, and it would be unforgivable deliberately to ignore them in favor of manufactured beverages made fashionable either by publicity campaigns or simply by passing snobbish fads.

Chapter 5

ALCOHOLISM AND CIRRHOSIS

Now that we have analyzed briefly in the preceding chapters the nature and the basic properties of the elements present in wine and the specific action of each on the human body, it is time to clear up an ambiguity which may be confusing readers.

There is a body of opinion, well meaning but possibly misinformed, whose adherents have been behind a series of campaigns against the consumption of wine, which they insist on including in the category of alcoholic drinks. Such people make two mistakes: on one hand they equate inert alcohol with wine, which is a living matter, and on the other hand they tend to confuse the honest taster of wine with an alcoholic.

We should never confuse a naturally produced wine with distilled alcohol. The former, which comes from the natural chemical and biological transformation of wine sugars, does not have the degree of toxicity of the latter, which is a carbonaceous chain ethanol capable of oxidizing.

It is now recognized that some 8% wines, apparently low in alcohol, are sometimes more toxic than 11% wines. For one thing, the nature of the vine plants plays an important part in the so-called alcoholic action of wine. Old French vine stocks which have for generations been cared for according to tradition yield a wine which is perfectly well tolerated by the human body and this is one of the reasons why, when we come to recommend remedies for the sick in the second part of this work, we choose only wines whose origin is exactly known.

One should also consider the manner in which a person drinks. On an empty stomach, alcohol travels very rapidly into the duodenum and in less than half an hour is absorbed by the blood. However if the stomach is full, the alcoholic absorption will take place much more slowly.

There is thus no comparison between an honest wine and a simple dilution of alcohol. Yet the opponents of wine drinking continue to brandish the specter of cirrhosis of the liver, which they claim to be on the increase and to affect only wine drinkers. It seems to be time to set the record straight. In fact a cirrhotic change in the liver may be due to many causes: we have known water drinkers affected by it.

First of all, if we rely on recent statistics, the yearly consumption of alcoholic beverages in France, expressed in terms of wine, is of the order of 700 cc per adult per day. Yet it takes a daily absorption twice as high as this to give rise to cirrhotic degeneration of the liver. Second, it should be pointed out that in France the majority of people suffering from alcoholism are to be found in cider-growing areas, or where a local "moonshine" is made; and that where winegrowing areas are affected, they tend to be areas where hybrids are cultivated. The same amount of wine drunk in places such as Bordeaux or Burgundy, where great wines are produced, does not appear to cause any serious trouble among its normal consumers.

It seems therefore that the degree of alcohol cannot be the point. Cirrhosis can also be caused by certain dietary deficiencies.

Ethyl alcohol or ethanol, the only form of alcohol ordinarily present in good wine, is a product of the normal fermentation of grape juice. But we should also remember that ethanol can be habitually present in the blood in an amount of 20 to 30 mg per liter. It represents then, a "toxin" which is a normal part of our tissues. This alcohol, provided that the daily dosage is equal to or lower than 1 gram per kilo (approximately 2.2 pounds) of body weight, plays the role of a reserve food, for once absorbed it is locally oxidized. The energy thus liberated can join in the process of cellular respiration, as the physiologists Hedon and Macabies have demonstrated. Moreover, according to Dr. de Bruigne, from a biological and medical point of view the 100 ml per liter (about 10 percent) of alcohol contained in wine bear no relation to the same amount of alcohol in a pure state. The alcohol present in wine is mixed with a whole living complex and it benefits the whole complex because of its real qualities.

The combination of alcohol and oxygen, allowing for an oxygenating process at the normal rate of 100 mg (.035 ounce) per kilo of body weight per hour, can be virtually complete when we drink wine in reasonable doses without other heat sources. To quote once more the two researchers mentioned above, "the freed energy can be fully absorbed in the progress of cellular respiration, thus providing a true source of calories."

Therefore, this natural alcohol, once assimilated by the body, is capable of substituting for about half of the basic organic expenditure of energy, or can be held in reserve for future use.

Professor Pages of Montpellier has in his time insisted that some natural elements found in wine actually constitute elements antagonistic to the alcoholic content, and protested that the chemical treatments all too often applied to wine today destroy this antagonistic factor. In effect, he argues that wine has never been proved beyond dispute to have been responsible for any case of alcoholism. We should admit, he says, "that there exists a lowering of the threshold of toxicity of wine which corresponds to the lowering of the consumer's resistance to intoxication."

This work, like studies done by others interested in the defense of quality wine, stresses that industrial wine-making, such as is practiced today, destroys this element antagonistic to alcohol. The result must mean a lowering of the threshold of toxicity of the wine, leading to possible symptoms of vitamin deficiency among consumers, or troubles affecting the balance of the central nervous system.

These pathological contingencies cannot be disregarded, and can only lend weight to the campaign against wine-drinking. But as we have already said, an honest wine, drunk in reasonable quantities, whose origin is known, such as those we recommend in the following pages, will never have bad aftereffects, only good ones.

And to conclude this short study, we shall quote this sensible remark by A. Gauthier who maintains that "if the danger of alcoholism exists in France, as everywhere else in Europe, it is due not to the consumption of wine, but rather to its too infrequent usage."

PART TWO

WINE AS THERAPY

"Un litre de vin contient la huitième partie de la ration alimentaire et le neuf dizième de bonne humeur."

Professor Landouzy

(A liter of wine contains one-eighth of our nutritional requirement and nine-tenths of good humor.)

INTRODUCTION

Before tackling the practical aspect of our subject—that is, the merits of the case that an honest wine is a precious supporting therapy to be recommended for various human ailments—we should be more specific about what we mean by the term "therapy" in this context.

In the following pages we intend (and we make a special point of this) to consider wine as a supporting remedy or therapy, not as a medicine capable of replacing, to the exclusion of all others, those which the patient is being prescribed by a doctor.

THERAPY AND MEDICATION

There is a certain distinction between these two nouns, which we shall now make for the purposes of the section of the book dealing with specific therapies.

If by "medication" we understand a simple or compound substance administered internally or externally as a *cure,* we shall use the term "therapy," on the other hand, to apply to anything which can be applied, generally, in the *treatment* of a morbid affection.

We do not intend in the following pages to make a full study of the therapeutic aspect of wine. Many excellent works have appeared on this subject and the curious or interested can refer to them.

We will limit ourselves to the simple presentation of the fermented juice of the vine as an adjuvant, or auxiliary therapy meaning according to one dictionary definition "anything that can determine a beneficial change in the economy of the whole body in general and of a particular organ, whether these means are hygienic, surgical, or pharmaceutical."

This is clear enough, and the second part of this work is written in this spirit.

CHOICE OF WINE

This second part will be presented in dictionary form, in two parts. This will make it easy for the reader to refer to. In the first part we will study the main ailments for which wine can be recommended, whether as a supplement to a diet or to the medicine already prescribed by the doctor, or as a prophylactic (preventive) agent.

For each of the wines chosen to alleviate one ailment or another, we shall attempt to explain the reason for our choice by stressing some of the inherent properties of the wine, indicating why it seems best adapted to combat the disease or the clinical consequences of the diathesis (bodily condition or constitution predisposing to a disease).

Obviously, because of the complexity of the chemical composition of wine and the nature of the soil, it is sometimes difficult to be able to state positively the reason why a particular wine, and not any other, acts as a therapeutic adjuvant. That it acts positively is certain, and other authors, greater authorities than we, have pointed them out. In any case, the interested reader who would like more detailed explanations can refer to the first chapters of this book.

In the second part of our dictionary we shall recall the main clinical uses of each of the wines previously recommended. Thus one will be able to see rapidly that Champagne, for instance, a natural product with specific qualities characteristic to the Champagne soil, the microclimate, and the nature of the particular vine stocks, can be recommended in many cases, ranging from recuperation after an operation to many serious diseases, particularly heart troubles.

DOSAGE

Every work of medical therapy includes, at the end of the pharmacological description of the medicine, and its administration to the patient, some lines devoted to its dosage: that is, the limits within which the active constituent can be used without danger to the organism, according to the way in which it is administered, the age, sex and general condition of the patient. We follow the same procedure in this work. We do this in order to maintain the idea of moderation, and to discourage excessive use of alcohol by any who might use a doctor's prescription as an excuse!

Let us first remember that wine must be drunk during meals, and not on an empty stomach. As for the amount allowed, we follow in general the advice of Professor Charles Fiessinger, who found that "a healthy man can drink without danger, while eating, 1 gram of wine alcohol per kilo of body weight per day."

Dr. E. Mauriac claims, and we leave him the responsibility of this statement, that we should "prefer a young 10% wine to an old wine laden with spirits and more toxic." And Professor Cruchet, who has specialized in the study of the amounts of wine tolerated by young people who are healthy and not offended by the smell or taste of wine, arrived at the following doses for children: a four-year-old can be allowed, per meal, between 12 and 15 grams (.5 ounces) of 10% wine (about 1 teaspoonful) diluted in 200 grams of water (1 cup); from six to fourteen this amount can be raised to 20 grams (.7 ounces); and from fourteen to eighteen the amount of wine may vary from 45 to 80 grams (1½ to 3 ounces) of red wine and 30 to 50 grams (1 to 1¾) of white wine per 300 grams (10 ounces) of water.

These figures are close to those given by Dr. Cayla and Dr. Dougnac, who suggest the following amounts of 10% wine per day, taken with the two main meals: 50 grams (1¾ ounces), between four and six years old; 100 grams (3½ ounces) up to eight years old; and 150 grams (5 ounces) from then on, progressively rising to 500 grams (1 pint) at the age of eighteen.

It is obvious that the figures mentioned above are relative, at least in their upper limits, and that a person can always lower the maximum dose depending upon the circumstances and the state of health. There are many patients who respond very rapidly to treatment and who can benefit from the positive effects of medicine only by taking it in small doses, smaller than those recommended by the laboratory or the doctor. It is the same with wine, and we intend to give only an idea of an average dosage for the average patient.

Now let us deal with the practical aspect of this work, which should be consulted just like a medical pharmacopeia, but with the difference that the active ingredients are exceptionally pleasant to take.

It is now up to the reader to discover for himself the age-old medical value of wine. It is to be hoped that he will find no less satisfaction than Pope Innocent VIII who, in a letter to the Duke of Burgundy thanking him for some Beaune wine, once wrote that the wine was "particularly favorable to my nature and temperament. I used it regularly during my last illness."

The nature of the disease was not specified, but we have no doubt of the therapeutic virtues that the Pope recognized in the juice of the vine.

MALADIES

(A)

ABDOMINAL DISTENSION

Exaggerated distension of the abdomen which, from a purely mechanical point of view, may be caused by an accumulation of gas from digestive fermentation, is often due to a sluggishness of nervous tone which reaches the abdominal sympathetic system. The same phenomenon can be observed in subjects who drink artifically carbonated beverages with their meals. In both cases the result is an unpleasant accumulation of air which must be evacuated.

Recommended wines
Alsace wines.
Why?
Because these wines act selectively on the nervous centers which control the digestion, encouraging absorbent and antacid properties.
Dosage
One or two glasses after meals.

AEROPHAGIA

Aerophagia is exaggerated swallowing of air, which in most cases results in a painful bloating of the stomach during or shortly after a meal. It most often occurs in nervous, worried people who are dissatisfied with their lives and who worry about a problem of affective or professional origin.

Recommended wine
Dry or brut Champagne.
Why?
First, because this wine has a euphoric effect on the psyche, without the disadvantages of classic tranquilizers.

Also, on the physical level, because the natural gas in Champagne promotes the mechanical action of the gastric wall. It stimulates physiological stomach contraction and thus the excess air is eliminated through the mouth. We should note that the natural gas present in Champagne which is found over three or four years as the wine matures in the cellars, is totally different from the artificial gas found in sparkling wines and factory-made mineral waters, which has been introduced rapidly under pressure. This type of product is always contra-indicated for the patient suffering from aerophagia.

Dosage
Two glasses per meal.

ALLERGY (tendency towards)

Allergic reactions, so common nowadays, are frequently linked with medicinal toxins, which sensitize the subject not only to the medicine but also to natural substances which once were harmless. They represent modifications caused in the body under the influence of a substance foreign to it, which is termed an "allergen." Reactions appear as secretions of the mucous membranes, or edema of the subcutaneous cellular tissue, produced by an excess of serous production. These unpleasant reactions do not prohibit the reasonable use of an appropriate wine.

Recommended wine
Médoc.
Why?
Because this wine is rich in natural potassium. This alkaline metal, in small doses, acts on water excretion problems, and thus on the phenomenon of water retention which is found in allergic reactions.
Dosage
Two glasses per meal.

ANEMIA

Anemia, or a pathological decrease in the number of red blood cells, manifests itself in a variety of disorders, among which are constant fatigue, vertigo, a lack of general tone, and sometimes hemorrhage.

It is therefore advisable—independent of other treatment proper for this type of disease—to give the patient a supplementary amount of iron.

Recommended wines
Graves wines.
Why?
Because of their iron content. The vine which

produces this type of wine is cultivated on pure sand containing iron particles in a soluble form. The iron level in the wine can sometimes reach 10 mg per liter.

Dosage
Two glasses per meal.

ANGINA PECTORIS (see CORONARY DISEASES)

ANXIETY

Some psychological illnesses, such as paranoias, or anxieties based on unreasoning fear, can be due in part at least to deficiencies in the organic salts normally present in the body. In most cases this is mainly a phosphate deficiency, phosphate being a basic food of the nervous system. A well-chosen wine will be of real help for the person who suffers from this type of affliction.

Recommended wine
Médoc.
Why?
Because of its richness in phosphorus in a concentration which can reach 0.03 to 0.05 grams, per liter, one-quarter of which is in organic form. This element represents a valuable remedy for the nervous cells.
Dosage
Two glasses per meal.

APPETITE (lack of)

During some illnesses it happens that the appetite is severely reduced. If the essential cause is not a serious organic lesion of the digestive system or a confirmed hepatic insufficiency, a well-chosen and judiciously drunk wine is quite capable of awakening appetite in the patient and stimulating his body functions once more.

Recommended wines
Light red, five-year-old wines (from the Médoc region).
Light white wines of moderate acidity and little sugar from the Anjou or the Graves region.
Natural sweet wines from Roussillon.

Why?
(a) Because the Médoc wine is a general tonic, rich in soluble iron and tannin;
(b) Because the white wines from Anjou and the Graves region act at the same time to stimulate digestion and sooth the stomach;
(c) Because the Roussillon wines (Banyuls or Maury) facilitate gastric secretion.

Dosage
Half a glass half an hour before meals.

ARTERIOSCLEROSIS

The pathological hardening of the arterial walls belongs to the group of symptoms which characterize the condition called "arteriosclerosis." But this diathesis, which is peculiar to civilized man, does not prevent him from drinking a correctly chosen wine in reasonable doses.

Recommended wines
    Muscadet.
    Rosé wines from Provence.
Why?
    (a) Because the vines which yield Muscadet grow on
        a decalcified soil poor in limestone;
    (b) Because rosé wines from Provence are at the
        same time diuretic and antitoxic.
Dosage
    Two glasses with meals, alternately one day Musca-
    det and the next the Provence wine.

ARTHRITIS (see URATES, excess of)

ASTHENIA (see FATIGUE)

AVITAMINOSIS (vitamin deficiency)

All good quality wines of a good vintage year contain
all the vitamins necessary for the human body, because
they come from sun-kissed grapes. The reader can refer to
the detailed information in the first part of this work.
Some disorders, which will be considered in the following
pages, are caused by general vitamin deficiencies. They
are dealt with under their proper headings, such as
PURPURA and RICKETS.

(B)

BILE INSUFFICIENCY

Any slowdown in the secretion of bile hinders good digestion. The symptoms are a certain sleepiness after meals especially in the early afternoon, flatulence, and constipation.

Recommended wines
Sweet white wines from Anjou and Vouvray.
Why?
Because these types of wine promote biliary secretion. However they must contain a little of the sulfur-dioxide which is added for their preservation. Hence they must be chosen well from a serious wine grower.
Dosage
One or two glasses after meals.

BRONCHI (diseases of)

Under this heading we mean all the acute diseases that can affect the respiratory apparatus, such as bronchitis, pneumonia, bronchial pneumonia, etc. These maladies, especially the last two, can be accompanied by lassitude, cardiac weakness and kidney malfunction, particularly when the now so popular antibiotics are used.

Therefore, as well as the classic therapy prescribed by the physician, we recommend the use of a well-chosen wine for as long as the illness lasts.

Recommended wines
  10% red Bordeaux or Burgundy wines.
Why?
  Because both these wines are rich in phosphorus, the properties of which we listed at the beginning of this work.
Dosage
  Heat the chosen wine in a double-boiler at 140°F; add 10 grams (1 teaspoon) of cinnamon, sugar, and lemon peel; drink three coffee-cupsful per day.

(C)

CARDIAC FAILURE

Any temporary or chronic failure of the cardiac muscle, which manifests itself in a whole series of symptoms so well known that it is not necessary to list them here, can be pleasantly and usefully alleviated by adding a well-chosen wine to the classic medications and diet.

Recommended wines
  Red Burgundy wines (Côte de Beaune and Côte des Nuits).
Why?
  Because these wines are especially rich in potassium, a metal which acts directly on cardiac automatism and on the tone of the cardiac muscle.

Dosage
Two glasses per meal.

CHOLESTEROL

This substance represents an organic waste whose excess in the blood leads to sclerosis of the arteries (see ARTERIOSCLEROSIS) as well as other circulatory disorders (see CORONARY DISEASE). It is the result of too rich a diet and too sedentary a life, a condition which in our contemporaries is commonly pathological.

Apart from regular exercises, and of diets low in fats (milk and butter especially), some wines can be recommended which will help eliminate excess lipids.

Recommended wines
Wines from the Val de Loire (Muscadet from Côteaux de la Loire or Sêvres-et-Marne).
Côtes de Provence.

Why?
(a) Because the vine stock which yields Muscadet grows on a humus poor in mineral salts and because the wine is acidic and not very sweet.
(b) Because the Provence wines are diuretic. Therefore they encourage the elimination of organic wastes.

Dosage
We recommend the alternate use of these two wines, drinking one one day and the other the next, in doses of two glasses per meal.

COLIFORM INFECTIONS

This disorder, often painful and accompanied by fever, is mostly of intestinal origin. It is due to a microorganism which multiples rapidly in an alkaline environment, and can have trying consequences for the patient, ranging from simple chronic fatigue to acute fever.

The addition of a well-chosen wine to the diet recommended by the physician, provided that there are no kidney lesions, will act preventively, according to Dr. Solier, and even contribute to cure, according to the works and research of Mrs. Jensen and Professor Masquelier.

Recommended wines
Dry white wine or dry Champagne.
Red Médoc.

Why?
  (a) Because, according to Dr. H. Galhinger, dry white wine contributes to the acidity of the humoral milieu, and it also is an excellent bactericide. It should be taken as a prophylactic by people who have a tendency to cultivate an excess of colibacilli.
  (b) Because red wine is both antimicrobian and remineralizing, since it is rich in oenotannins and mineral salts. It will act as a therapy to complement the specific medical treatment.

Dosage
Two glasses per meal of one or the other wine depending on whether the aim is preventive or therapeutic.

COLITIS

This chronic inflammation of the intestinal tract, so common these days, is usually accompanied by muco-membranous reactions and by spasmodic abdominal pains. In most cases the principal cause is an imbalance in the autonomic nervous system, due to emotional conflicts or simply to the life that we are forced to lead today.

Recommended wines
   Dry white wines with a low alcohol content, particularly dry Gaillac.
Why?
   Because the natural components of this type of wine contribute to the balance of intestinal tone; and also because of the euphoric effects of wine in general and of Gaillac wine in particular.
Dosage
   One or two glasses per meal.

CONSTIPATION

Regular intestinal sluggishness can be due to a number of causes, the most important one being atony of the smooth muscles of the walls of the digestive tract.

An immoderate use of laxatives intended to fight this condition may, after a certain time, actually encourage this sluggishness so that the person suffering from this affliction finds he cannot escape from a vicious cycle which in the end must prove detrimental to his health.

Encouraging the moderate use of wines particularly suited to digestive sluggishness can only have a beneficial

67

effect on intestinal evacuation.

Recommended wines
   White wines from Anjou or Vouvray.
Why?
   Because, low in alcohol, lightly sweetened, rich in tartrates and glycerine, they act as stimulators of the intestinal mucous.
Dosage
   Two glasses per meal.

CONVALESCENCE

Malaise, which follows an acute or long illness has always been alleviated by the use of so-called "tonic" wines. The old pharmacopeia which, despite what we may say now, was full of good sense, counseled them; and these natural wines have been wisely and widely recommended by doctors throughout the ages. Today we are privileged to live in the so-called "scientific" age, so we select instead stimulant medicines, dull-tasting vitamin pills, or liver extract ampuls which are not very tasty either.

But a good wine full of sun and rich in natural elements drawn from the nutritive soil will bring the convalescent something to warm up his body and his soul.

Recommended wines
   Bordeaux red wines from the Médoc region.
   Roussillon wines.

Why?
  (a) Because wines from the Médoc contain an average of 100 to 300 (1 to 3 percent) mg of phosphate per liter, associated with potassium action.
  (b) Because Roussillon wines are rich in tonic elements such as natural sugar.

Dosage
  One glass before meals and with cheese at the end of the meal.

CORONARY DISEASES

Inflammation of the coronary arteries which feed the cardiac muscle can be due to various causes which we do not intend to enumerate here. Let us only recall that the consequences of this circulatory problem usually manifest themselves as painful attacks in the precordial region, such as angina pectoris, or as a tendency to embolisms, such as myocardial infarct. Dr. Nussbaum, after recent statistical studies, noticed that the countries which drink the most wine have the lowest incidence of coronary affections. According to him, wine could play a preventive role and also be useful in the medical treatment of cardiac disease, which is getting more and more common today.

However, it must be understood that wine should not be administered during an acute cardiac attack.

Recommended wines
  Dry or brut Champagne

Why?

Because this type of wine is rich in potassium
bitartrate. This salt has a favorable action on muscle
tone, and on the ability of the muscles to contract.
Therefore these wines help to strengthen the cardiac
systole, and thus consequently effect better oxy-
genation of the heart.

Dosage

One or two glasses before meals.

CYSTITIS

Irritation and inflammation of the bladder can have
many different causes which the doctor or specialist will
identify and treat. Cystitis can be due to the presence of
urinary stones, to a coliform or any other microbe
infection.

Outside, of course, of the acute and painful attack, the
patient may be allowed to drink wine, especially because
of the particular bactericide and diuretic virtues of wine
which we have stressed on several occasions.

Recommended wines

Sweet or semisweet white wines from Anjou.

Why?

Because these wines, like all wines in general, are
antiseptic. Moreover, because of their special composition, these wines contribute to modifying the
humoral milieu whose alkaline content encourages
the rapid multiplication of microbes.

Dosage

One or two glasses per meal.

(D)

DECALCIFICATION

The loss of calcium can have serious consequences, primarily on bones but also on cartilage and ligaments. A great many pharmaceutical products are now available for people suffering from this type of mineral deficiency, but their therapeutic use does not prevent the patient from regularly drinking an adjuvant wine well chosen for its remineralizing virtues.

Recommended wines
Red Bordeaux wines (Saint-Emilion).
Saumur wines.
Sweet wines from Roussillon.
Why?
Because the vines which produce these different wines grow on calcareous soil. The choice between these types of wine is a matter of individual tolerance and personal taste.
Dosage
Two glasses with meals for the Saint-Emilion and the Saumur wines.
One glass before meals for the Roussillon wines.

DEMINERALIZATION

Excessive loss of mineral elements, not only calcium (see DECALCIFICATION), but other elements useful to

WINE AS THERAPY

the organism, can be observed in older people during some acute or chronic diseases. These minerals must be replaced, and wine is an ideal means towards doing so.

Recommended wines
Red Burgundy (Gevrey-Chambertin or Clos Vougeot).
Châteauneuf-du-Pape.
Why?
Because these wines are particularly rich in mineral salts (limestone, silica and phosphate).
Dosage
One or two glasses after meals.

DIABETES

This term covers two pathological diseases, both of which are characterized by excessive urination accompanied by excessive thirst and abnormal appetite. But in current practice the term refers especially to a disorder called sugar diabetes (mellitus), which is caused by poor metabolism of glucose, creating an excess of sugar in the blood as well as in the urine.

Apart from a very strict diet, especially as far as carbohydrates are concerned, and the use of the classic therapeutic medications, some wines are indeed recommended for patients suffering from this disease. This statement, which may seem bold, is supported by the results of the work of Professor Soula and Dr. Baisset of Toulouse, both of whom have been particularly interested in this problem, as well as that of Dr. Weissembach of Paris.

Recommended wines

Young red wines with a moderate percentage of alcohol (Bordeaux or Sancerre).

Why?

There are many reasons, according to the afore-mentioned researchers. First, wine, because of its very composition, acts as a nutriment which replaces the starchy food forbidden in the diet; it also prevents diabetic coma by opposing the formation of ketonic bodies; by its vitamin content it stimulates the combustion of sugars and fats; and last, it facilitates the metabolism of nitrogenous food and lipids which, in a diabetic's diet, replace the forbidden carbohydrates.

Dosage

An average of 800 grams (about 28 ounces) of red wine per day to be divided between the main meals. This must be included in the dietary allowance medically prescribed.

DIARRHEA

Reactions of the intestinal mucous membrane, with their unpleasant and sometimes painful consequences, can either be acute and momentary, or can be due to a chronic tendency. The wines recommended below are thus of different character, according to the problem.

Recommended wines

In case of acute diarrhea, light red wines, such as a young Beaujolais.

In case of chronic diarrhea, old wines with an

average amount of alcohol, such as the Médoc wines.
Why?
Because both these wines contain tannin in variable
proportions which increase with the age of the wine.
Dosage
One glass before and after meals.

DYSPEPSIA

Habitually bad digestion has its principle causes (for
there may be many) in disorders of the motility of the
gastric musculature, or in a slowdown of the normal
secretions of the stomach.

In both cases a well-chosen wine will pleasantly
remedy this inconvenience, which often affects the whole
personality of the person who is affected.

Recommended wines
Dry or medium dry white wines from Anjou or
Vouvray.
Why?
Because of their composition, these wines act as an
excitant on the smooth stomach muscles and on the
quality of gastric secretion.
Dosage
One or two glasses at the end of meals.

(E)

ECZEMA

This skin disease can appear in different forms. In most cases it is characterized by red spots on the skin and by itching blisters which can be closed and dry or open and oozing.

Recommended wines
Either light white or light red wines.
Why?
Because these wines are not strictly forbidden to peoples affected by this skin disease. Moreover, because of their content in elements such as manganese and sulfur as well as in natural vitamins, these wines give the patients the elements they may be lacking.
Dosage
An average of half a liter per day divided between the two main meals.

ENTERITIS

This inflammation of the intestinal mucous membrane is generally accompanied by pain and a certain tendency to diarrhea. Independent of the appropriate medical treatment and a proper diet, the reasonable use of certain well-chosen wines will be beneficial for those who suffer from this rather obstinate illness.

Recommended wines
Red Médoc wines, old and light.
Why?
Because these wines are rich in oenotannins, the properties of which we have studied in a preceding chapter.
Dosage
Two glasses per meal.

EYES (diseases of)

It may seem strange that wine may affect the ocular apparatus in any way. However, some authors recommend a reasonable use of this beverage for patients suffering from asthenia or fatigue, and who are unable to make sustained efforts of concentration.

Recommended wines
Light red Bordeaux or Burgundy wines.
Why?
Because they contain potassium which acts on muscular tone by encouraging both the tonicity and contractility of ocular muscles.
Dosage
Two glasses per meal.

(F)

FATIGUE

We should first clarify what we mean by fatigue, a term which recurs so often in present-day conversation. For our purpose it is a simple physical exhaustion due to excessive muscular activity. As for nervous or psychological fatigue, with its repercussions on the patient's nervous system, we will treat it under NEURASTHENIA.

Recommended wines
Bordeaux wines from the Saint-Emilion region.
Burgundy wines from the Côte de Beaune region.
Why?
Because these wines are rich in tannin, in phosphorus, and in iron in its soluble form. They are therefore restorative and act as a tonic, bringing to the tired body the elements which it lacks.
Dosage
One glass before and after meals.

FEVER

Any abnormal increase in temperature, especially if it lasts, is a sign of poor health. It should not be ignored and calls for medical advice since its causes could be many.

In many cases this phenomenon indicates symptoms of lassitude; that is, a certain lack of energy which should be compensated for to avoid more serious consequences.

Apart from the medications recommended and pre-scribed by the doctor, a good wine will help stimulate the patient's own biological defenses, and thus a return to a normal temperature.

Recommended wines
Dry or brut Champagne.
Why?
Because these wines contain, among other things, two important elements for a feverish person: phosphorus, which is eminently stimulating, and sulfur in its sulfate of potassium form, whose de-toxifying action on the body has been established.
Dosage
One bottle per day, taken in doses of one glass every hour.

FLATULENCE

The accumulation of gas in the stomach has already been treated under the heading AEROPHAGIA, to which the reader should refer. Here we will consider the same problem, but localized this time in the intestine.

Recommended wines
Dry, young, white Alsace wines.
Why?
Because their content in mineral salts and oligo-elements constitutes a precious contribution to combating any tendency towards intestinal slug-gishness, which affects the smooth muscles of the

digestive tube as well as the secretion of local juices. In fact, a deficiency of these substances is one of the main causes of this condition.

Dosage
Half a bottle per day divided between the two main meals.

(G)

GALLSTONES

According to Professor Castaigne there are generally no mineral deposits (urates, oxalates) in the biliary tract or gall bladder of an alcoholic, or of someone who drinks a lot of wine. Without advocating excess, we can deduce that the moderate use of a good wine allows a true drainage of the gall bladder, as we have already stressed in the appropriate diet for the patient suffering from insufficiency of bile.

But in the present case the choice of wine will be different.

Recommended wines
Dry white wines, low in alcohol, from the Sancerre or Pouilly region.
Why?
Because, if we rely on the Similarity Principle so dear to doctors of homeopathy, these wines grow on a soil rich in silica. This "stony" element is perfectly adapted to the patients with organic "stones" and it

insures both their dissolution and their expulsion.

Dosage

One or two glasses after meals.

GOUT

It is normally assumed that this painful affliction of pathological origin, which affects certain joints, particularly those of the big toe, is found only in healthy eaters and hearty drinkers.

But this is not always the case. People who follow a strict diet and drink only water can also be subject to gout attacks. And hereditary factors obviously also play a role. However, the gout-prone terrain is very close to the arthritic terrain, in the sense that the patient has an excess of uric or oxalic acids which must be eliminated from the body.

Therefore we must choose a wine appropriate to this diathesis, and obviously not drink it during acute and painful attacks.

Recommended wines

Light white wines from the Sancerre or Pouilly regions.

Rosé wines from Provence.

Why?

Because thanks to their alkaline properties and the presence of alkaline carbonates, these two wines help to dissolve uric and oxalic acids. Moreover, they encourage a good diuresis.

Dosage

Two glasses per meal.

(H)

HEMORRHAGE (gastric)

A special paragraph must be devoted to this type of hemorrhage, so commonly associated with stomach ulcers. It eventually causes a more or less serious anemia which further complicates the poor physical condition of the patient. In this case, too, wine is far from being forbidden. *However, a doctor should be consulted immediately by anyone vomitting blood.*

Recommended wines
Red Bordeaux or Burgundy wines.
Why?
Because experience has proven that these wines, which are rich in tannin, have styptic, hemostatic virtues—that is they help to staunch bleeding.
Dosage
Half a bottle, to be drunk slowly during the day.

HEMORRHAGE (tendency to)

We are of course not trying here to base an entire therapy for hemorrhage on the virtues of wine. But there is a whole category of people who tend, with the slightest bump, to show ruptures of the small superficial vessels of the skin, what we usually call bruises. In other cases, after a serious loss of blood following an injury the patient should be given a normal number of red cells to replace those lost in the accidental hemorrhage. In both cases wine has a role to play.

Recommended wines
Semidry Champagne wines.
Wines from the Côte de Beaune.
Why?
(a) Because they are rich in natural sugar and alcohol, the semidry Champagne wines help quickly to strengthen a person weakened by loss of blood;
(b) In a second stage, to reestablish a normal level of red blood cells, the red wine mentioned above will help because of its iron and mineral content;
(c) Independent of this restorative activity, we should mention that thanks to the oenotannins red wine contains factor P, which encourages an increase in capillary resilience, and whose action complements that of vitamin C (see Chapter 2 of the first part of this work).

Dosage
Two glasses per meal.

HYPERCHLORHYDRIA

An excess of hydrochloric acid secreted in the stomach, most often due to a pathological increase in stomach activity, calls for some well-chosen wines.

Recommended wines
Red or white wines with a low acid level, such as wines from the Saumur region.

Very sweet white wines, such as the Sauternes, Barsac, or Sainte-Croix-du-Mont.

Why?

Poor in tannin, but grown in calcareous soil, these different wines are all rich in calcium which acts as a sedative on the excitability of the nerve cells.

Dosage

One or two glasses per meal.

HYPERTENSION (high blood-pressure)

Blood-pressure higher than the physiological norm (which can vary from individual to individual) does not always indicate a lesion of the circulatory system or the cardiorenal apparatus. In many cases, especially in our troubled times, it may be only a passing disorder linked to excessive nervousness or hyperemotionalism. In any case the diagnosis of the cause will be made by a physician.

If we refer to the conclusions drawn by Professor Charles Laubry and by Dr. J. Lemand, high blood-pressure does not necessarily follow from excessive wine drinking. The normal and reasonable use of wine must not be systematically excluded in this case, since wine has a hypotensive effect due to its alcohol fraction.

Recommended wines

Light and dry white wines with low alcohol content, such as the Sancerre, Pouilly or Alsace wines.

Why?

Because these wines are diuretic. They cause a release of urea chlorides and uric acid. Therefore they help to eliminate the excess of organic liquid which promotes the blood plethora, an important factor in the tendency towards hypertension.

Dosage
Two glasses per meal.

HYPOCHLORHYDRIA (see STOMACH, sluggishness of)

HYPOTENSION (low blood-pressure)

The drop of vascular tonus with consequences such as fatigue, psychological asthenia, and low morale calls for the bottled sunshine of wine.

Recommended wines
Red Burgundy wines, wines from the Côte de Beaune.
Banyuls wines.

Why?
Because all these wines are rich in potassium, and thanks to this metal they act on the weakness of the nervous and muscular systems.

Dosage
Two or three glasses per meal of Burgundy.
One glass of Banyuls before meals.

(I)

INFARCT (tendency towards)

Congestion of a main artery such as the coronary artery which feeds the cardiac muscle carries consequences which are now too well known for us to stress.

A patient who has already suffered from this circulatory trouble does not have to banish wine from his normal diet. Quite to the contrary, a reasonable consumption, far from being harmful, can, according to cardiologists such as Professor Charles Laubry, be one of the auxiliaries of classic treatment, and act as a healing agent on the psychological level. If we also refer to the statistics published by Dr. Nussbaum, it has been established that the countries with the highest consumption of wine have a comparatively low incidence of coronary disease.

Recommended wine
Dry Champagne wine.
Why?
Because it is rich in potassium bitartrate which plays an important part in the mechanism of cardiac contraction.
Dosage
One or two glasses before and after meals.

INFLUENZA

This seasonal, infectious viral disease can in certain cases deeply disturb the vital tone of the patient. One notices or feels a painful state of fatigue, with cardiac weakness and breathing difficulties. The body is in urgent need of fast, effective and specific sources of energy. This is even more necessary nowadays when the fashionable therapy consists of prescribing massive doses of antibiotics, much beyond what may be needed.

Recommended wines
Wines from Côtes du Rhône.
Why?
Because these wines are rich in alcohol and are therefore stimulants and rich in calories. They also contain natural antibiotics which are therefore well tolerated.
Dosage
We recommend the following recipe during the feverish stage. Heat in a double-boiler at 140°F a bottle of the wine listed above; add 1 tablespoon of cinnamon, 5 teaspoons of sugar, and some lemon peel. Drink half a bottle per day in three or four equal portions.

(L)

LIVER (sluggishness of)

At the risk of evoking loud protest from "enlightened"

dietetic amateurs (there are more and more of them in our time of organized planning, not to say puritanism), we shall aver that good wine is far from being contra-indicated for people with a sluggish liver. However it is important to stress that the hepatic failure we are now considering should *not* have been caused by cirrhosis in either its earliest or especially in its developing stage.

We should recall that sluggishness of the liver is often indicated by a whole variety of symptoms, many of which have already been mentioned in this work under different headings. If the complaints are specifically linked with some major discomfort, we invite the reader to refer to these sections (see AEROPHAGIA, APPETITE [lack of], BILE [insufficiency], CONSTIPATION, DYSPEPSIA, in particular). But if the case is simply one of mild hepatic sluggishness (a vague symptom, of course, but quite real for the person suffering from it), we recommend the drinking of certain wines in order to enliven the often trying and boring diet which is prescribed.

Recommended wines
    Dry Champagne wines.
Why?
    Because these wines are rich in sulfur, which is usually found combined with potassium as potassium sulfate. In the preceding pages we have seen that this mineral plays an important role as a detoxicant, and that thanks to its action the liver can itself act as an antitoxin. It therefore both has a cleansing function, and protects against microbic or organic poisons.

Dosage
One or two glasses in the middle or at the end of meals.

LOSS OF WEIGHT

Any loss of weight can be due to a series of causes, which range from a normal loss of appetite to more serious metabolic troubles.

Independent of the appropriate therapy prescribed by the doctor on the basis of his causal diagnosis, we can recommend to any patient affected by weight loss a suitable wine.

Recommended wines
Côtes de Beaune.
Why?
Because these wines are rich in iron as well as mineral extracts, among which is calcium; a mender of bone cells.
Dosage
Two glasses per meal.

(M)

MENOPAUSE

The end of reproductive activity in women is often accompanied by all sorts of more or less annoying problems, which may sometimes be alleviated by hormonal therapy prescribed by the general practitioner or the gynecologist.

However a low-calorie diet, often recommended because of a tendency to gain weight, can, with no problems and indeed with advantage, be made more palatable by a well-chosen wine.

Recommended wines
Bordeaux wines from the Médoc region.
Why?
Because they are rich in oenotannins which act through the medium of factor P on the resistance of the capillaries. One of the symptoms proper to menopause is the fragility of the small blood vessels, which tend to break under the slightest contact or pressure, thus causing bruises under the skin.
Dosage
Two glasses per meal.

(N)

NEPHRITIS

Any acute or chronic injury of the kidney tissue affects what is an essential function of the body. There can be many causes for such injury, and we shall not discuss them here. In acute attacks, especially if there is albumen in the urine, wine must be absolutely banned from the diet. But this is not the case when the nephritis is chronic, even if there is albumen in the urine. The patient can then drink a correctly chosen wine in moderation.

Recommended wines
Light red Bordeaux 10% wine.
Light white wine from the Saumur region.
Why?
(a) Because it contains mineral salts, red Médoc contributes to the regeneration of kidney cells;
(b) Because light white wine from the Saumur region is diuretic and slightly alkaline.
Dosage
One or two glasses per meal.

NERVOUS DEPRESSION

We cannot ignore the great disease of this century: a century of almost daily "progress," and constant (although fragile) improvements in our standard of living, yet which forces upon us an almost unbearable speed-up in the pace of life.

We have never before used so many artificial tranquilizers and tonics as we do now, while we complacently proclaim the benefits of industrial, technocratic civilization, and earn unheard of profits for its promoters and sycophants.

The deficiency sometimes responsible for these states of psychic fatigue is phosphorus deficiency—phosphorus being an essential nutriment of the nerve cell.

Recommended wine
Red Médoc wine.

Why?

Because the glycerine it contains combines in the intestine with the phosphates of the fermented grape juice, to form glycerol-phosphates of natural lime, which have tonic virtues and which do not interfere with the functional integrity of the nervous system.

Dosage

One or two glasses before and during meals.

NEURASTHENIA

This is a condition which more than any other justifies a reasoned and reasonable use of wine.

The *taedium vitae*, the aversion to life which the Romans knew well, may have many causes, physical as well as psychological. But even when there are irreversible lesions of the central nervous system, the point of departure of personality change, most authors agree on the restorative and tonic virtues of wine.

Recommended wine

Blanquette de Limoux.

Why?

This white wine, recommended in the eighteenth century to neurasthenics by Dr. Barthez of the Montpellier medical school because of its high phosphate content, acts as a true nutriment for the central nervous system, the cerebral cells as well as the nuclei at the base of the brain and the spine.

Dosage

Half a bottle per day, apart from meals.

(O)

OBESITY

Excess weight often constitutes a true infirmity that contributes in large part towards ruining the life of the person suffering from it. It also affects the general health.

We shall deal under SLIMMING DIET with the problems caused by too restrictive a diet, and how to correct this by the use of a well-chosen wine. But if the obese person does not or cannot lose weight, he should still not deprive himself of wine, as long as the wine is correctly selected as part of a calorie allowance.

Recommended wines
Rosé wines from Provence.
Dry white wines from the Sancerre region.
Why?
Because these wines are low in sugar and alcohol. They also have diuretic properties and thus facilitate the evacuation of organic wastes such as uric acid. Finally, they act as a stimulant on the endocrine glands whose action is often slowed down in obese persons.
Dosage
One bottle per day, divided between the two main meals.

OLD AGE

It has often been written that wine is the milk of the elderly person, and it is true in the vast majority of cases.

An old person has an increased need for calories since he suffers, even if healthy, from a slow-down in his metabolism which is accentuated with the passing years. Therefore he needs to supplement this deficiency, and wine seems the obvious choice of remedy since it also brings mineral elements such as calcium and phosphorus which are indispensable.

Recommended wines

Red wines from the Alose-Corton region.

Light white dry wines such as the natural (non-carbonated) Champagne wines.

Why?

(a) The Burgundy wines for their part are rich in mineral elements which an old person often lacks;

(b) The white wines, rich in sulfur, bring the older person, who tends to suffer from a deficiency of this metalloid, an adjuvant necessary for his metabolism, in particular for restoring and maintaining suppleness in the tissues;

(c) Lastly, wine is a tonic for the elderly. Plato himself was of the opinion that: "Wine, both a sacrament and a relaxant for men of old age, was given to them by a god as a remedy for the austerity of old age, so that oblivion of affliction removes from his soul consciousness of the extremity of his condition."

Dosage
One or two glasses with meals, alternately red wine one day and white wine the next.

OSTEOPOROSIS

The diffuse decalcification of some important bones of the skeleton, often due to an endocrine malfunction, can benefit not only from the prescription of an appropriate therapy but also from a complementary diet rich in substances to feed the bone tissue, such as calcium and phosphorus. These elements are biologically interconnected: that is, calcium is only really beneficial for the body in the presence of phosphorus.

A well-chosen wine will provide complementary amounts of these two elements, in a natural state.

Recommended wines
Red Bordeaux wines from the Médoc region.
Red Burgundy wines from the Côte de Nuits region.
Why?
Because these wines are produced from stocks growing on calcareous terrain, and contain an average of 100 to 300 mg (1 to 3 percent) of phosphorus per liter.
Dosage
Drink alternately two glasses of Bordeaux wine with the main meals one day, and the same amount of Burgundy the next.

(P)

PHOSPHATE LOSS

Loss of phosphates in the body shows itself, chemically speaking, in an excess of this element in the urine. The patient complains of abnormal fatigue and nervous depression, and urine analysis is the usual way to confirm the doctor's diagnosis.

Here again, and apart from the medical treatment, some wines can be added to the prescribed treatment, with beneficial results.

Recommended wines
Dry or medium-dry Champagne, depending on individual taste.
Why?
Because these wines contain phosphorus, 30 to 100 mg (about .3 to 1 percent) per liter. They are also light and tonic, both for the body and the mind.
Dosage
One or two glasses after meals.

PNEUMONIA (see INFLUENZA)

POSTOPERATIVE CONVALESCENCE (see CONVALESCENCE)

PREGNANCY

During pregnancy, unless there are serious organic lesions or other disorders capable of modifying normal gestation, the pregnant woman may drink wine. Two factors are to be considered. First, the mother's need for mineral salts and vitamins to prevent weakening of the skeleton and degeneration of the tissues. Second, the necessity to stimulate the antitoxic function of the liver, whose role is to destroy maternal and fetal toxins.

Recommended wine
Light red, 10% Bordeaux wine.
Why?
Because the light red Bordeaux is rich in calcium and oenotannins, and also because it facilitates antitoxic liver function.
Dosage
Two glasses per meal.

PURPURA

This affliction is essentially characterized by red skin blemishes due to the rupture of small capillaries inside the derma. These ruptures then cause small localized hemorrhages under the skin.

Obviously this ailment, or rather this predisposition, should be medically checked and treated. But in addition a well-chosen wine may be advised.

Recommended wines
Bordeaux wines from the Saint-Emilion region.

Why?

Because they are rich in oenotannins and in factor **P**, which is one of the antiscorbutic factors. A vitamin P deficiency involves, among other things, a lowering of the resistance of the capillaries, and therefore a tendency to hemorrhage.

Dosage

One or two glasses per meal.

(R)

RHEUMATISM (chronic)

This affliction, so common today, calls for both medical and physiotherapeutic treatment, hydropathic or marine cures depending on the case, and often for a strict diet which can sometimes cause some deficiencies detrimental to the patient. Sulfur, whose detoxifying action is of capital importance, is an indispensable element for patients suffering from chronic rheumatism, and many spas recommended for the rheumatic have sulfurous waters.

The euphoric quality of wine is also important to the patient suffering from arthritic conditions, especially when his mobility is reduced and his morale consequently low. So for biological as well as psychological reasons, the patient should be allowed to drink a well-chosen wine.

Recommended wines

Dry light wines, such as the natural (noncarbonated)

wines from Champagne.

Why?

Because they are rich in sulfur and mineral elements.

Dosage

Two glasses per meal.

RICKETS

This affects children during their period of growth, and is due to a lack of calcium and phosphorus in the system. The young person suffers from a vitamin D deficiency— vitamin D being essential to the fixation and action of these elements, which in turn are indispensable to bone tissue. We can add to the patient's diet a certain quantity of wine which is a natural source both of the metal and the metalloid.

Recommended wines

White Bordeaux wines from the Entre-Deux-Mers region.

Red Bordeaux wines from the Médoc region.

Why?

(a) Because the first of these two wines comes from stocks growing on soil made of clay and lime-stone, therefore rich in calcium;

(b) Because the second one contains, as we have already mentioned several times, 100 to 300 mg (about 1 to 3 percent) of phosphorus per liter.

Dosage

After the age of five, the child can have 50 grams (about 1-3/4 ounces) of Bordeaux wine before meals, alternately the white wine one day and the red the next. After the age of ten, the dosage can be increased to a maximum of 100 grams (about 3.4 ounces) per day.

(S)

SALMONELLA

Under this general heading we find a whole series of intestinal problems of bacterial origin, whose clinical symptoms are those of the classic typhus.

Recommended wines
Old red wines from the Médoc region, well preserved.
Why?
Because they are rich in phenolic compounds whose bactericide properties were detailed in the first part of this work.
Dosage
Half a bottle per day to be drunk with the two main meals.

SENESCENCE (see OLD AGE)

SLIMMING DIET

Any weight excess (see under the heading OBESITY) requires the prescription of a correctly apportioned diet low in sugars and fats.

The wine to go with this type of diet must follow the

same imperatives. But a little wine with these rather ascetic meals will bring a little cheer to the strictness of the prescribed diet.

Recommended wines
Wines from the Côte d'Or.
Why?
Because the composition of these slightly colored wines encourages the metabolism of fats, and retain considerable nutritive value.
Dosage
Two glasses per meal.

STOMACH OR HIATUS HERNIA

Hiatus Hernia—which becomes more and more common as the men, and especially the women, of today benefit from so-called progress—is the result of muscular laziness which affluent living helps to promote. In addition to the physical exercises recommended and the diet, which has to be adapted to the degree of impairment of the digestive organ and muscular reactions, a correctly prescribed wine will both help, and be appreciated by, the patient.

Recommended wine
Medium-dry Champagne.
Why?
Because this disorder is often connected with the nervous system (pneumogastric or sympathetic). It is therefore advisable to prescribe a wine with a low alcohol content and low degree of acidity, but

which is not too young or too rich in tannin. These properties are all found in the wine recommended above. Moreover, Champagne contains a certain amount of potassium (between 30 and 100 mg [about .3 to 1 percent] per liter), whose action on the tone and flexibility of muscle is well known—the stomach after all is a muscle.

Dosage

Two glasses per meal.

STOMACH (sluggishness of)

Good digestion is often even more important than good food. Digestion is a process which takes place in an acid milieu. Poor digestion is often due either to lack of tone in the gastric muscle, or to an insufficiency of digestive secretions, and these two phenomena are, in most cases, associated.

So a cure is a matter of restoring to the weakened stomach its normal muscular tone and a properly acid milieu.

Recommended wines

Dry or brut Champagne.

Why?

Because these wines have a favorable pH, equal on the average to 2.85, and because they act on muscular tone because of their tannins, glucides, and natural carbon dioxide. Moreover, they contain potassium as bitartrate, whose effect on the flexibility of muscle fibers is known. Finally, they accelerate the secretion of ferments which act on

101

the digestion of albuminoid substances such as meat and fish. They have a definite advantage over the often recommended carbonated waters, which are mostly artificially prepared and poor in natural chemical elements.

Dosage

One or two glasses after meals.

(T)

TONSILITIS

Inflammatory affections of the pharynx and tonsils are usually accompanied by difficulty in swallowing and fever. Patients can greatly benefit by adding wines to any medicinal treatment, especially because of the bactericidal properties of wine.

Recommended wines

Red Bordeaux wines from the Médoc region.

Red Beaujolais wines.

Why?

Because the tannin content of these wines gives them decongestant qualities, and also because like all wines they are bactericidal, antiseptic, tonic, and diaphoric.

Dosage

Warm up 500 grams (about 1 pint) of a 10% wine chosen according to the personal taste of the patient; add 10 grams (about 1 teaspoon) of cinnamon, sugar, and lemon peel; drink two half-bowlsful three times per day.

TUBERCULOSIS

Lung specialists, among them Dr. Nustal de Montana, seem to agree that the use of wine is far from being contra-indicated for persons carrying the Koch bacillus.

Recommended wines
Red Bordeaux wines from the Médoc region.
Brut Champagne wines.
Why?
   (a) Because they are rich in calcium, the Médoc wines promote the remineralization of the organism. Because of their phosphorus content they act as a euphoric element on the nervous system, a far from negligible factor in hastening recovery. And finally, like all other wines they have bactericide properties.
   (b) As for the brut Champagne wines, they are rich in potassium which acts as a tonic agent in patients weakened by a long illness. Moreover they are particularly recommended if drunk iced during the hemorrhages which can often complicate the pulmonary form of the disease.
Dosage
For the Bordeaux wines, half a bottle per day to be divided between the two main meals.
For the Champagne, three or four glasses in the course of the day.

TYPHOID FEVER (see SALMONELLA)

(U)

URATES (excess of)

The uric diathesis, which falls into the category of autointoxications known under the more general term of arthritis, is often due to metabolic dysfunctions affecting more specifically the nitrogenous substances.

The patient has a tendency to retain the urate crystals rather than eliminate them and they accumulate in his joints, or in the kidney canals or in the urinary ducts.

Some American dieticians, concerned about the acidity of wine, recommend for such patients cider vinegar, which is rich in potassium. A well-chosen wine is nevertheless recommended.

Recommended wines
　　Red or white wines from the Saumur region.
　　Gros Plant from the Nantes region.
Why?
　　(a) Because the Saumur wines come from stocks cultivated on calcareous, sometimes silica-rich soils. Very low doses of these two elements help assimilation and metabolic processes, and their diuretic action activates the normal secretion and excretion function of the kidney.
　　(b) As for the Gros Plant, it is rich in potassium bi-tartrate, which gives it highly diuretic properties.

104

Dosage
Two glasses per meal of one or the other.

URINARY STONES

The solids made up of salts such as urates and oxalates or phosphates resemble small grains which can lodge themselves in the urinary ducts or in the bladder. They should not however prevent the patient from drinking a correctly chosen wine.

Recommended wines
Dry white wines, low in alcohol, from the Sancerre or the Pouilly region.

Why?
The reasons for prescribing and selecting these wines are the same as those given for the treatment of gallstones.

Dosage
One or two glasses with or after meals.

URTICARIA (tendency towards)

Wine is gifted with immunizing properties in regard to substances capable of causing allergic reactions; that is, reactions of humoral hypersensitivity, of which urticaria is one of the symptoms.

Dr. Weissembach cites as an example patients sensitized to strawberries, a fruit which triggers flare-ups of urticaria. He noticed that patients were free of allergic reactions if they took the precaution of soaking the berries in red wine for about fifteen minutes before eating them.

Professor Loeper, quoted by Dr. Dougnac in his thesis on wine, noticed the same disappearance of urticaria in two patients subject to the allergy after eating fish: if they took the precaution of drinking wine with these dishes they were exempt from allergic reactions.

Recommended wines
Light red wines with strawberries.
Light white wines from the Sèvres-et-Marne region with fish.
Why?
Because of the antiallergenic properties of wine.
Dosage
One large glass per meal in both cases.

PART THREE

A MEDICAL LEXICON OF WINES

"Go thy way, eat thy bread with joy, and drink thy wine with a merry heart."

(Ecclesiastes IX, 7)

INTRODUCTION

In conclusion, in the last part of this essay on oeno-therapy, it seems useful to give a list of wines and their medicinal properties according to winegrowing areas, as a guide to patients in choosing suitable drink for the table. This synoptic list of wines and their regional locations will also give an idea of the large selection available, and is intended as a complement to the detailed exposition in Part Two.

CLINICAL INDICATIONS

Winegrowing Regions	Clinical Indications
ALSACE	Abdominal distension
	Abdominal flatulence
	Hypertension (high blood-pressure)
ANJOU	Appetite (lack of): Anjou rosé or white
	Bile (insufficiency): White Anjou
	Constipation: White Anjou
	Cystitis: Medium-dry white Anjou
	Dyspepsia: White Anjou
BORDEAUX	Allergies (tendency towards): Médoc
	Anemia: Côtes de Graves
	Anxiety (neurosis): Médoc
	Appetite (lack of): Médoc, Graves
	Bronchia (diseases of): Médoc
	Coliform Infections: Médoc
	Decalcification: Saint-Emilion
	Depression (nervous): Médoc
	Diabetes: Red Médoc
	Diarrhea: Médoc

Winegrowing Regions	*Clinical Indications*
BORDEAUX	Enteritis: Médoc
	Eyes (diseases of): Médoc
	Fatigue: Saint-Emilion
	Hemorrhage: Saint-Emilion
	Hyperchlorhydria: Sauterne, Barsac
	Menopause: Saint-Emilion
	Nephritis: Médoc
	Osteoporosis: Médoc
	Pregnancy: Médoc
	Purpura: Saint-Emilion
	Rickets: Entre-Deux Mers, Médoc
	Salmonella: Médoc
	Tonsilitis: Médoc
	Tuberculosis: Médoc
	Typhoid: Médoc
	Urticaria (tendency towards): Médoc
BURGUNDY	Bronchitis: Beaujolais
	Cardiac (insufficiency): Côte de Beaune, Côte de Nuits
	Demineralization: Gevrey, Chambertin, Clos-Vougeot
	Diarrhea: young Beaujolais
	Fatigue: Côte de Beaune
	Hemorrhage: Côte de Beaune
	Loss of Weight: Côte de Beaune
	Old Age: wines from the Alose-Corton region
	Slimming Diet: Côte d'Or
	Tonsilitis: Beaujolais

CLINICAL INDICATIONS

Winegrowing Regions	*Clinical Indications*
CHAMPAGNE	Aerophagia
	Coliform Infections
	Coronary Disease
	Fever
	Hemorrhage (tendency towards)
	Infarct (tendency towards)
	Old Age
	Phosphate Loss
	Rheumatism (chronic)
	Stomach, or Hiatus Hernia
	Stomach (sluggishness of)
	Tuberculosis
CÔTES DU RHONE	Demineralization: Châteauneuf-du-Pape
	Influenza
LOIRE Valley	Arteriosclerosis: Muscadet
	Cholesterol: Muscadet
	Decalcification: Saumur wine
	Dyspepsia: Vouvray
	Nephritis: Saumur wine
	Urates (excess of): Saumur wines, Gros Plant
PROVENCE	Arteriosclerosis
	Gout
	Obesity
SANCERRE	Gallstones

Winegrowing Regions	*Clinical Indications*
SANCERRE	Gout
	Hypertension (high blood-pressure)
	Obesity
	Urinary Stones
SOUTHWEST	Appetite (lack of): sweet Roussillon wines
	Colitis: Gaillac wines
	Convalescence: Roussillon wines
	Hypotension (low blood-pressure): Banyuls
	Neurasthenia: Blanquette de Limoux

SUPPLEMENT ON OTHER EUROPEAN WINES

In a book as essentially practical as this one, it is simply not possible to study the medical and oenologic content of all the many wines produced throughout the continent of Europe: there are too many vineyards in too many winegrowing areas, and to list all the suitable wines would only confuse and bore the reader.

But to supplement the French wines—themselves only a selection of the many there are to choose from—I have made a selection of the principal wines produced in the other main winegrowing countries. For each of these, Italian, German, Swiss, Spanish and Portuguese, I give below the medical properties, and the French equivalent, so that it will be easy for the reader to refer to Part Three of this book, *A Medical Lexicon of Wines,* for its therapeutic application.

As an example, Italian Asti may be compared with French Champagne, whose clinical indications are listed on page 113. The reader will then be able to check in the corresponding entries in Part Two for details of treatment and dosage.

ITALIAN WINES
The Italian peninsula produces as much wine as France, if not more. The following are the most important names.

Chianti, the best known wine, has a high reputation and comes from Tuscany. The vines are grown in rocky soil, sometimes so stony that it is necessary to cut into the rock in order to plant the stock. It is the rock that gives Chianti its special medical qualities.

Certain types of Chianti red wines, such as the Vini di Pasta, are young and light and fresh, resembling the French Beaujolais wines; others on the other hand, like Vino d'Arrosto, are stronger and full-bodied, like the wines of Southwest France, particularly the Roussillon wines referred to several times in the text. As for white Chianti, which comes from a variety of Trebiano grapes, it is very dry with a strong flavor and can best be compared with the wines of the Loire valley.

Varolo is grown in the south of the province of Piedmont. Its alcoholic content is about 15%, and its medicinal qualities are similar to those of the French wines grown along the Rhone valley.

Asti comes from the region of Turin and is a white sparkling wine made from a special variety of Muscatel grape, sometimes mixed with Pinot and Riesling. In certain respects it resembles young Champagne, and has similar therapeutic applications.

Valpolicella originates from Venetia, and is a light red wine comparable with the French Médoc from the Bordeaux region.

Marsala is a Sicilian wine grown from particular vines such as those of Catarratto, where the wine industry was originated in the eighteenth century by an Englishman, a certain "John Woodhouse, Purveyor of Wines at Liverpool." Catarratto is a light spicy wine whose medicinal qualities are again comparable with those of the soft wines of Roussillon. Similarly stimulating to the spirits and the appetite are the wines of Malvasia, which have the same therapeutic qualities, and are grown from vines descended from those known to the ancient Greeks in the famed vineyard on Lipari, the largest of the Aeolian Islands. These wines are amber-colored, and heavy, rich in alcohol, so they are best kept for convalescents from serious illness, and even then prescribed in moderate doses not exceeding one or two glasses a day.

GERMAN WINES

The German wine industry is much smaller than either the French or Italian, and since the vineyards are situated in the northern part of the hemisphere they are more exposed to bad weather, particularly frost. White wines were produced on the Rhine and the Moselle as far back as the Roman conquest, and though they declined after the fall of the Roman Empire viniculture was once more encouraged by Charlemagne. Most of the vintage wine cultivated even today on the banks of these two rivers comes from Riesling stock whose origin dates back to the arrival of the Roman legions.

Riesling wines have a low alcoholic content, but a certain freshness that appeals readily to the palate. The Rhineland wines are the most important.

Rheingau wines, from the world famous vineyards in the region between Wiesbaden and Rudesheim, are fruity and full-bodied. Nearby are also the Schloss Vollrade and Steinberg winegrowing areas.

Middle-Rhine wines, grown between Coblenz and Bacharach (probably itself named in honor of Bacchus), have more color than those of the Rheingau, but less flavor.

Hesse wines, of which the best known are Niersteiner Riesling and Liebfraumilch, are fresh and fruity. They may be compared for their therapeutic qualities with the wines of Alsace, to which they are immediate neighbors.

Palatinat wines, both red and white, are produced on the sheltered slopes of the Haardt hills where the climate is mild and the soil fertile. They are comparable with French light *vins ordinaires* from the Angevin district, and have similar medical attributes.

Moselle wines, grown on the sunny banks of the Rhine tributary, the Moselle, delight the eye with their color, a pale greenish-yellow. They are all produced from Riesling stock, and are light, low in alcohol content and have the characteristic Riesling bouquet. It is not possible to name all of them, since there are so many, but it is worth mentioning those of Bernkastel, particularly Bernkastel Doktor and Piesporter. Like the Rhine wines, their medical properties are similar to those of the wines of Alsace; or those of Sancerre.

SWISS WINES

The Swiss vineyards are small and they do not produce enough wines even for local consumption. But the tourist on holiday in Switzerland who may wish to choose a local wine with a therapeutic content, would do well to remember the name of Fendant du Valais, a white wine made from Chasselas grapes, which were introduced into Switzerland by an army officer in the time of Louis XIV. It is a dry, light wine that leaves an aftertaste I can best describe as that of stones and steel: comparable in its therapeutic qualities with a light Burgundy.

The best known classic red wine is Dôle, full-bodied, high in alcohol content, and grown from a mixture of Black Pinot and Gamay stock. Its medical application is similar to that of a red Burgundy.

SPANISH WINES

It is not possible to name all the wines produced in Spain, but the following are perhaps the best known among connoisseurs abroad.

Sherry comes from the region around Jerez de la Frontera, and is produced from white Palomino among other grapes. The soil of limestone and clay determines the wine's therapeutic qualities. Sherry is remarkable for its rich color, ranging from pale yellow through various golden tints to dark brown.

Manzanilla is grown in vineyards neighboring those of Jerez, but it is generally paler and dryer. Both Sherry and Manzanilla are rich in minerals and benefit patients suffering from anemia and mineral deficiencies.

Malaga wines grow close to the coast of the Mediterranean, and are sweet and rich in color, again ranging from pale yellow to dark brown. They may be compared with French wine from Banyuls, and have similar medical properties.

PORTUGUESE WINES

Port, from the Duro valley, is without doubt the most celebrated of the wines of this Atlantic country. It is made from black grapes, and its color varies between ruby red and burnt topaz. From a medical point of view, it is to be reserved for patients convalescing from serious illness, or suffering from low blood pressure or nervous breakdown.

Minho wines too have undoubted therapeutic value: the Vinho Verde, white, young and light with low alcohol content, is an excellent diuretic.

Dao wines are grown on the same plains that produce the Port wines. They come from a mixture of red and white grapes, and are soft wines comparable with French Burgundy for their therapeutic properties.

Madeira, from the island of flowers, is a wine the color of pale straw, which may be prescribed for convalescents and for sufferers from anemia.

There are other countries in Europe that produce wines, many of which can meet the needs of the sick as well as please the taste of the connoisseur. But it is to be hoped that the above survey will serve at least as an introduction to the many and varied uses of wine as a therapy. In every case, however, my advice remains: enjoy your wine, but USE . . . DON'T ABUSE.

AMERICAN WINES FOR HEALTH

Julius L. Jacobs

INTRODUCTION

With his exhaustive and scholarly work, Dr. Maury has most assuredly performed a valuable and humanistic medical service. The medicinal and therapeutic values of wine have long been acknowledged in Europe and, more recently, in America as well. Only within the past quarter-century, however, once the wicked spell of the "Prohibition" of all alcoholic beverages in the United States was broken by its repeal in the early 1930s, did the appreciation of wine and its utilization as a valuable adjunct to modern medicine receive proper recognition.

The question has often been asked in the U.S.A.: "When, in fact, did the use of wine as a medical agent first become known?" And the most truthful and accurate answer is, of course, in Biblical times, as well as in ages of the Greeks and the Romans, then throughout the Middle Ages and into the modern era. Closer to home, in American Revolutionary days the first great statesmen—George Washington, Thomas Jefferson, Benjamin Franklin, to name just a few—all were distinguished political leaders dedicated to the everyday use of wine in their own lives both for pleasure and for health reasons.

The magnificent and redoubtable patriot and drafter of

the Constitution, Jefferson, wrote a letter to President James Monroe in 1817, when Jefferson was seventy-six years of age, describing his daily routine, and he said: "Like my friend Dr. Benjamin Rush I have lived temperately, eating little animal food. I double however, the doctor's daily glass-and-a-half of wine, and even treble it with a friend. . . ."[1]

In the nineteenth century, the cultivation of vines and the importation of *vitis vinifera* grape cuttings from Europe were already taking place by the 1830s and the 1840s. For some wine enthusiasts, however, such as the brilliant lawyer and landowner Nicholas Longworth of Ohio, the native grape, the *vitis labrusca*, seemed sound enough. This flamboyant and dynamic gentleman, the great-grandfather of a later Nicholas Longworth (speaker of the House of Congress in the administration of President Coolidge [1924]), planted twelve hundred acres of vineyards in Ohio in the 1840s. He had decided, in his own words, that by producing light table wines he could woo Americans away from the use of "hard liquor." In this instance Longworth utilized a new "wonder grape" of that era, the native Catawba. Longworth produced both table wines and champagnes.

Gradually, as time went on, cultivation of the grape on the far West Coast and particularly in California became of paramount importance to the production of fine wines and brandies in America. It had begun as far back as the 1770s when the Spanish Franciscan friar Junipero Serra first planted grapevines in that state. But only in the early 1820s and 1830s were the commercial planting of grapevines and production of acceptable wines achieved.

Soil, sunshine, favorable winds, and the skill of the

vintner, in California as well as in all wine producing countries, are the basic ingredients which serve beneficient ends—resulting in the marvelous nectar we drink in the form of wine.

Perhaps the most important ingredient is the soil, and in California the great variety of soils results in the tremendous scope and variety of grapevines planted and the bountiful harvests. But it is also the climate and the micro-climates which make possible the growth of the species of *vitis vinifera,* often called the European grape, in California. In no other section of the United States has this species been so favored by nature and resulted in such a happy and overwhelming cultivation of vineyards and production of wines.

Granted the marvelous good fortune of fine soils and salubrious climate, California wines have prospered for much more fundamental reasons. As Professors V. L. Singleton and M.A. Amerine have reminded us, grapevines are adaptable to most well drained soils—even if they may be relatively infertile. With extensive root systems they are able to withstand lack of rain more than other fruit crops. Where irrigation can be employed, the lack of rainfall is not a great hindrance. In California, the prospect of summer rains is often quite remote—differing from conditions in Europe.

Since the wine grapes of California are of the *vinifera* species, they are actually the first cousins—or possibly the grandchildren and the scions of their aristocratic French ancestors. Some cuttings such as the fabulous Chateau d'Yquem of Sauternes, were brought over before the dawn of the twentieth century. Others came as early as the 1850s and some later, in the 1880s. The point is: red for red, white for white, these closely related wine grapes of California also transmit the equivalent—or almost equivalent—taste values and sensory impressions of their French counterparts. And since this is the case, is it too far fetched to suggest that the phenols, the tannins, the enzymes, the vitamins may not also bear some equivalency to the medical values attributed by Dr. Maury to the wines of France?

To illuminate the subject, we present a table which gives an approximation of the wines of California which resemble those of the Bordeaux, the Rhone, the Loire, the Beaujolais, and the other distinguished grape and winegrowing regions whose lineage goes back centuries. And for what it is worth, there is also a "mystery grape" in California—the much acclaimed Zinfandel, once erroneously believed to have been brought from Hungary by a famous nobleman, Agoston Haraszthy. Today, however, it is believed to be not Hungarian in origin, but rather a strain similar to a southern Italian grape variety called *primitivo*. At any rate it makes remarkable wine, it is indigenous to California and it has a close resemblance to the wines of the Cotes du Rhone and the Mercureys of Chablis.

Remembering there is no exact "match-up" of wines that are grown in different climates and soils, we offer a personal listing of California counterparts to the wines of France.

FRANCE AND CALIFORNIA WINES
SOME COMPARISONS

Area of Origin and Grape	*Recommended Counterpart and Suggested Origin*
ALSACE	
Gewurztraminer	Gewurztraminer, Sonoma
Muscat d' Alsace	Muscat of Alexandria
Pinot Blanc	Pinot Blanc, Monterey
Pinot Gris	Emerald Riesling, Santa Clara
Riesling	Johannisberg Riesling, Monterey
Sylvaner	Sylvaner, Monterey
Pinot Noir Rosé	Pinot Noir Rosé, Sonoma
BORDEAUX - White	
Sauvignon Blanc	Sauvignon Blanc, Livermore
Semillon	Dry Semillon, Livermore
BORDEAUX - Red	
Bourg, Blaye, Entre-Deux-Mers, etc.	Ruby Cabernet, Santa Clara California French Colombard
Graves	Zinfandel, Amador
Médoc	Cabernet, Napa
Pomerol	Merlot, Napa
St. Emilion	Cabernet, Sonoma
SAUTERNE/BARSAC	Johannisberg (white) Riesling, Monterey

Area of Origin and Grape	*Recommended Counterpart and Suggested Origin*

CHABLIS

Meursault	Chardonnay, Sonoma
Puligny-Montrachet	Chardonnay, Napa
Maconnais/Chalonnais	Pinot Blanc, Napa
Mercureys	Pinot Blanc, Sonoma

BEAUJOLAIS

Beaujolais Supérieur	California Zinfandel or California Gamay Beaujolais Nouveaux
Beaujolais Village	Gamay, Napa
Moulin-a-Vert, Brouilly	Gamay Beaujolais, Monterey

BURGUNDY

| Côte de Nuits | Pinot Noir, Napa |
| Côte de Beaune | Pinot Noir, Sonoma |

CHAMPAGNE

| | Champagne, Napa-Sonoma-Mendocino California Sparkling Muscat |

JURA

| Château-Chalon | Chilled California Dry Sherry |

LANGUEDOC

| Corbiere | Grey Riesling, Monterey Barbera, Santa Clara |

126

Area of Origin and Grape	Recommended Counterpart and Suggested Origin

LOIRE

Sancerre Pouilly-Fumé	Fumé Blanc, Napa
Tours/Anjou	California Grenache Rosé
Vouvray (dry)	Chenin Blanc, Napa
Vouvray (sweeter)	California Chenin Blanc
Bourgueil/Chinon	California Zinfandel
Coteaux de Layon	Sauvignon Blanc, Livermore
Saumur sparkling wine	California Champagne
Muscadet	French Colombard, Mendocino

RHONE

Condrieu	California White Zinfandel
Côte Rôtie	California Petite Sirah
Hermitage (red)	Petite Sirah, Livermore
Hermitage (white)	California White Zinfandel
Châteauneuf-du-Pape	Petite Sirah, Napa and Sonoma
Châteauneuf-du-Pape (white)	California Sauvignon Blanc
Tavel	California Grenache
Côte du Rhone	California Zinfandel
Voaucluse muscat	Muscat Canelli

WINE AND MODERN MEDICAL RESEARCH

Wine and its medical values have always played a significant role in modern research connected with California's wine industry. Over a forty-year period from the 1940s to the mid 1970s the Wine Advisory Board authorized research into the broad fields of alcohol and the medical aspects of wine. Part of this had to be done, unhappily, to counteract the strange and unsubstantiated charges sometimes made against the use of wine on the basis that this beverage could "cause" disease. Into this research were poured hundreds of thousands of dollars, thousands of hours of research time and of course the benefits included many scientific papers by eminent researchers. Another portion of the research was initiated for more constructive purposes—to ascertain the beneficial effects of wine in specific types of medication.

Perhaps the most succinct and accurate summing up regarding the significance of wine in medicine is to be found in Amerine and Singleton's discussion on wine as alcohol where the authors conclude: "alcoholic beverages and wine in particular have a long and honorable history of usefulness in both lay and formal medical therapy. With the development of modern more specific and more potent drugs, the use of alcohol in medicine has declined but not disappeared. Alcohol has been said to be the most thoroughly studied, most valuable and safest tranquilizer known. It helps reduce pain, anxiety and tension. In a palatable form such as wine it can serve as a tonic. Use of wine, especially for the aged and convalescent, can lend interest and flavor to the diet. The appetite and feeling of well-being can be stimulated. Dry wine can be a source of non-sugar calories as well as dietary variety for diabetics and others on restricted diets. Wine is normally low in sodium and high in potassium (unless stabilized by sodium ion-exchange). This and alcohol's effect in dilation of peripheral blood vessels make wine worthy of consideration for persons with arteriosclerosis and hypertensive vascular conditions. Alcoholic beverages, moderately used, may help induce sleep, stimulate gastric secretion, and produce mild diuresis. Properly handled and with consideration for contra-indications, wine and other alcoholic beverages have medical utility."[2]

Dr. Milton Silverman of California, distinguished researcher and former head of medical research for the Wine Advisory Board of California, properly assessed the role of wine in the practice of medicine. In essence the renowned pharmacologist and wine writer asserted: "Because of its low alcohol content and its content of protective chemicals, and also because of cultural and sociological factors ... wine may ... be described as a pharmaceutical agent of major importance, and moreover, an agent which may serve as the most effective preventative of alcoholism known to medicine. Beyond a certain point, wine and plain alcohol differ. More wine continues to give more relief, while more plain alcohol or more of a comparable beverage begins to give more tension."

In collaboration with still another distinguished pharmacologist and former vice president of the University of California Medical School, Dr. Chauncey D. Leake, the two scientists write that the chemistry of alcoholic beverages and their pharmacological and clinical effects are "superb subjects which fully warrant scientific study. It appears to be time," declare Silverman and Leake, "that intelligent people should understand the effects of alcohol—not only as alcohol, but as beer, wine, and distilled spirits—on the human body and human society. Only through such knowledge can [it] be used beneficially for both the individual and his society—in health and disease."

The scientists concede that the application of alcoholic beverages to the maintenance of health and the treatment of disease is scarcely new, since in Europe it has been "widely accepted by competent physicians for centuries."[3]

The importance that wine has assumed in medical practice in California may be found in the establishment of one typical group—the Society of Medical Friends of Wine, organized in San Francisco thirty-seven years ago. This society is composed of several hundred leading medical practitioners. Regular meetings of the medical group are invariably predicated upon the presentation of specific papers concerning scientific and medical subjects which emphasize or take cognizance of the role of wine in society. There also are vintage tours to learn more about the wine districts and the specific values of wine, as well as specialized wine tastings conducted not only for the medical profession but for special audiences.

As delineated in its statement of purpose, "the object of the Society of Medical Friends of Wine is to stimulate scientific research on wine, develop an understanding of its beneficial effects, and encourage an appreciation of the conviviality and good fellowship that are a part of the relaxed and deliberate manner of living that follows its proper use."

As an example of the scientifically oriented subjects which are often featured in the lectures of the Medical Society, John J. Power, Ph.D., professor of food science at the University of Georgia, spoke on "Wine Components" before the 98th quarterly dinner meeting in San Francisco, discussing the esthetics and utility of these components. In a summing up, Dr. Power commented: "Pasteur stated that wine is the most hygienic of beverages. Our work on wine showed that the pigments of wine are among those substances contributing to the hygienic properties . . . all of the action does not reside in the alcohol. The pigments are not only esthetically pleasing, they serve the very utilitarian purpose of making wine a safe beverage." Dr. Power also added that in his research study he had a good bit of success in establishing that wine pigments have significant action against pathogenic microorganisms, "whose activities we prefer to do without."

In evaluating the specific areas in which wine plays an important role, one professional approach which has interested thousands of physicians, surgeons, and medical groups lays stress upon the following:

In the Normal Diet

In the normal diet, wine furnishes useful energy for body maintenance and muscular work—plus significant quantities of B vitamins and mineral elements.

In the Bloodstream

Consumption of wine gives relatively low, safe blood

131

alcohol levels—blood tests show absorption is even slower when wine is taken with meals.

As Tranquilizer

In form of wine, alcohol is one of the oldest, most widely used and probably safest of all tranquilizers—its efficacy confirmed in modern laboratory research.

In Diabetic Control

Dry wine has established values in diabetes nutrition (insulin is not required in alcohol metabolism)... it can be incorporated in balanced diabetes diets.

Reducing Emotional Tension

Coronary disease is relatively infrequent in wine-using communities. Wine is helpful in reducing emotional tension in hypertension, angina, obliterative vascular disease—even in obesity diets.

Geriatrics and Convalescence

In geriatrics and treatment of convalescents, wine can play a most valuable therapeutic role—as tranquilizer, mild sedative and appetite stimulant, an aid in the digestive processes, nutritive adjunct.

"In Sickness and in Health . . . "

So goes part of the traditional wedding ceremony

which unites two people in the bonds of matrimony.

And, so, in many ways the medical ritual of the physician attending his patient also comes down to the sagacious use of wine in the practice of sound medicine. And here are listings of some of the physiological effects of wine, as worked out over a long time span by reliable authorities.

In Health

Wine: Acts as a tranquilizer
       Stimulates appetite
       Provides quickly available nutritive energy
       Furnishes B-Vitamins
       Dilates cutaneous blood vessels
       Increases secretion of digestive enzymes
       Stimulates liver and pancreas
       And—serves as a mild diuretic

In Disease

Wine: Controls emotional tensions
       Serves as a mild sedative
       Improves the palatability of restricted diets
       Produces relaxation in hypertension and coronary diseases
       Provides a useful energy source in diabetes
       Maintains obese patients on reducing diets
       And—increases fat absorption in malabsorption syndrome

These are, perhaps, abbreviated conclusions as to wine's major roles in the normal routine of health and disease; but could it be set forth better in fewer words, for those who follow the use of words with fascination? Along these lines, we also quote with great admiration the comments of the noted physician William Dock, M.D., appearing before the proceedings of the First International Symposium on Wine and Health, which took place at the University of Chicago Center for Continuing Education several years ago. Dr. Dock, who was at the time the chief of medical services, Veterans Administration Hospital, Brooklyn, spoke before a distinguished group of American colleagues on the role of wine in the care of heart disease, cancer, and stroke, and at the conclusion of his remarks made the sagacious comment: "As physicians, as disciples of Hippocrates, it is our task to care for every aspect of the life of our patients, but particularly to make sure that they receive correct nutritional and therapeutic agents which do the most good with the least harm. The products of the vine are invaluable in heart disease, cancer and stroke, and we may say, with Omar Khayyám, 'I often wonder what the vintners buy one half so precious as the thing they sell.' "

Summing up the findings of the First International Symposium, Dr. Salvatore Pablo Lucia, emeritus professor of medicine at the University of California's San Francisco Medical Center, in the book *Wine and Health* declared: "We have . . . the recorded findings of some of the most noted observers of wine and noted researchers of wine-and-health in the world today. . . . These confirm the blessings of wine as told in the Bible—but with scientific objectivity, and with an accuracy that no Biblical sage could have commanded. Thus the confirmations of the health giving and medicinal values of wine stem from experiments performed in chemical and physiological laboratories, and from clinical experiences by doctors in hospitals, nursing homes, and 'extended care' facilities. I envision important additions to this knowledge within the next few years. . . ."[4]

WINE IN GERIATRICS

American society appears to be developing a larger and larger proportion of elderly inhabitants. Lowered birth rates and higher levels of medicine which reduce mortalities have contributed to an older population group. Medicine is increasingly faced with the challenge of caring for its elderly citizens—sometimes patronizingly described as "senior citizens." And wine plays an increasingly important role in keeping these persons happier and healthier.

One of the more compassionate views of wine and its effects on older citizens is found in the statement of Dr. Robert Kastenbaum, Ph.D., professor of psychology at Wayne State University. In a panel on the use of wine in hospitals and nursing homes, Dr. Kastenbaum stated: "Wine is a food and a drug. But it is also a concrete symbol of adult mutual gratification. There is a world of difference between ordering an old man to take his medicine, and inviting him to have a drink. The former action confirms his opinion that he is an impaired organism to be processed and serviced by impersonal means. The latter action suggests that he is still regarded as a grown-up, one who is capable of giving and receiving adult gratifications."

A graphic illustration of the moods and feelings of

older patients who were given wine in an extended care facility compared with those who were not, has been described by Dr. Vincent Sarley, M.D., of the Wright-wood Extended Care Facility of Chicago. Dr. Sarley referred to a pilot study at this institution, a ninety-bed hospital. One question concerned nursing care. Of those not given wine, only 33 percent felt they had had "enough" nursing care. Of those who had been offered and accepted wine in a ninety-day investigative period, an overwhelming 93 percent felt they indeed had had enough nursing care. On the question of properly cooked food, 43 percent of the nonwine drinking group said that it had not been properly cooked. But 100 percent of the wine drinkers enjoyed their food as being properly prepared! The same general statistics of disapproval and approval were determined in connection with questions of "Was your bed comfortable?" and "Was the atmosphere quiet or noisy?" The difference in mood among those drinking quite modest amounts of wine was quite striking.

Scores of larger hospitals and other institutions specializing in care of patients are now offering wine on a voluntary basis today in California and in other states. This also extends to nursing homes as well.

The Bulletin of the Society of Medical Friends of Wine has recently reported that this custom, which originated in the San Francisco Bay Area twenty years earlier, is now spreading to other parts of the nation. In the sister-state of Oregon, the Bulletin learned, nearly forty hospitals and health care facilities have applied for licenses to serve wine, after the state's legislature amended the law to provide a special hospital wine license.

Most patients in such enlightened institutions, with approval of their physician, of course, may receive red, white, or rosé wines with their meal trays. In a recent report of more than two thousand patients in San Francisco area institutions, those questioned were found to have positive feelings about their surroundings and their food.

Dr. Robert Stepto formerly of the University of Illinois Medical School, member of the Chicago Board of Health, and a clinical professor of obstetrics and gynecology, said of the medical-hospital use of wine: "I believe we should intensively promote the therapeutic uses of wine. This would involve education of hospital personnel, physicians, and patients."

SPECIFIC WINES FOR HEALTH

In European countries and other regions where wine use is commonplace, there is a fairly standardized prescription of specific wines for specific medical or health reasons. As a helpful adjunct in the promotion of tranquility, for example, one medical authority recommends: "To achieve proper tranquilization in the home, a four-ounce serving of wine can be taken on an empty stomach, or eight ounces can be taken with food." Before a meal, good results are achieved by the service of dry Vermouth, dry Sherry, and sometimes a brut Champagne. If accompanied by appetizer foods, such vinous beverages have the capacity to stimulate the appetite.

Sweeter wines, however, (cream Sherries, Ports, and sweet Vermouths) have an opposite effect. One of these wines, Port, however, is particularly favored for another purpose. As Dr. S.P. Lucia states in *Wine & Your Well Being,* "for pure calming ability at bedtimes, the sweet dessert wines seem ideal. The alcohol content is about 20 percent. Greater concentrations would flow too quickly into the bloodstream and would quite likely produce stress. Lower concentrations require too great an intake (of fluids) imposing increased needs for late-hour visits to the bathroom, thereby partially defeating the purpose. Port has a deserved reputation as a mild, safe agent for inducing sleep. The usual serving is 3-1/2 ounces about a half hour before retiring." Lucia adds that sweet Sherries and Muscatel are also useful in the late afternoon of a lengthy day that has been challenging and tiring.

Table wines are of extreme value in adding to the sense of well-being and physical ease. Where, at one time, Port was regarded of value in treatment of iron-deficient (anemic) persons, today modern analysis indicates that other wines are "substantially richer in iron, with an average of 4.7 mg. per liter in dry white table wines and 6.0 in dry red table wines."[5]

Many persons in the United States are under physicians' orders to carry on a restricted or low sodium diet program. Where this occurs, wine is often indicated to "provide relief from the dullness and unpalatability of many such dietary prescriptions." In their studies, pharmacologists Leake and Silverman find that average concentrations of sodium are 8 mg. per 100 cc. red table wines, 10 for sweet white table wines and the highest, 16 mg. for rosé table wines.

Many patients, those who suffer from malaise, postoperative symptoms, worry and personal anxieties—or even those who unwisely undertake lengthy and strenuous diets—often find their appetite seriously diminished. There is a need for stimulus in this respect—and wines play an important role here. Dr. Lucia points out that dry Sherry is "as different from white wine as could possibly be imagined." At the same time, this doctor of preventive medicine asserts, it is also effective at rousing the appetite. It contains more alcohol and greater variations in sugar content than the white table wines, and therefore as an appetizer works "far better" for those who prefer fuller flavor and higher alcohol content than offered by white wines.

Red wines are also extremely useful in health practices. Old red table wines, specifically, appear to be particularly good choices where diabetics are concerned, since they contain very minute amounts of reducible sugar. Such California wines as Cabernet Sauvignon and Zinfandel, with a good deal of age behind them, or a well-cellared Pinot Noir, would seem to fit this bill of particulars, while a California Chardonnay or White Riesling might help more in tempering the appetite.

It has been well documented by medical researchers that sparkling wines have an excellent role to play in allaying or reducing morning sickness in pregnancy, and may also prove remarkably effective in seasickness and averting nausea.

There still remains another valuable use of wines in medicine and this is wine in its general, nonspecific aspect. We refer to wine as an antibiotic, and Dr. Lucia points out that within the past decade important discoveries have shown that the phenolic compounds of wine, including the pigments, are the most potent antibacterial agents. These compounds—phenolic acids, anthocyanins and tannins—when isolated from wines appear to inhibit test cultures of many strains of bacteria, according to Dr. Lucia, "including those responsible for the gastrointestinal diseases which wine has been known to neutralize throughout the ages."

This noted California medicine-and-wine researcher also stresses the role of wine as a solvent or carrying agent for medicines. Since this usage has received "legal benediction" in the U.S., several types of wines are now commonly used, such as the white wine preparations which carry Vitamin B materials. Lucia concludes that wine is "the ideal agent in which to present the many substances of medicinal importance which must be introduced into the human body."

In essence, sound medical practice over the long span has always allotted an important role to the moderate use of wines. And increasingly, as more and more is being learned about the more than three hundred separate components of wine, Americans along with millions of other wine consumers are gaining new insights into wine's overall healthful benefits.

NOTES

1. Nunez, Bernard E., *Vinifera Wine Growers Journal*, Vol. 1, No. 1, Spring 1974, London.

2. Amerine, M. A. and V. L. Singleton, *Wine (An Introduction for Americans)*, University of California Press, Berkeley, 1971.

3. Silverman, Milton and Chaucey D. Leake, *Alcoholic Beverages in Clinical Medicine.*

4. Lucia, Salvatore P., ed., *Wine and Health,* Pacific Coast Publishers, Menlo Park, California, 1969.

5. Lucia, Salvatore P., *Wine & Your Well Being,* Popular Library, New York, 1971.

THERAPEUTIC INDEX

Abdominal Distension, 57
Aerophagia, 57
Allergy (tendency towards), 58
Anemia, 59
Angina Pectoris (see Coronary Disease), 60
Anxiety, 60
Appetite (lack of), 61
Arteriosclerosis, 61
Arthritis (see Urates, excess of), 62
Asthenia (see Fatigue), 62
Avitaminosis, 62

Bile Insufficiency, 63
Bronchi (diseases of), 63

Cardiac Failure (insufficiency), 64
Cholesterol, 65
Coliform Infections, 66
Colitis, 67
Constipation, 67
Convalescence, 68
Coronary Diseases, 69
Cystitis, 70

Decalcification, 71
Demineralization, 71
Diabetes, 72
Diarrhea, 73
Dyspepsia, 74

Eczema, 75
Enteritis, 75
Eyes (diseases of), 76

Fatigue, 77
Fever, 77
Flatulence, 78

Gallstones, 79
Gout, 80

Hemorrhage (gastric), 81
Hemorrhage (tendency to), 81
Hyperchlorhydria, 82
Hypertension (high blood-pressure), 83
Hypochlorhydria (see Stomach, sluggishness of), 84
Hypotension (low blood-pressure), 84

Infarct (tendency towards), 85
Influenza, 86

Liver (sluggishness of), 86
Loss of Weight, 88

Menopause, 88

Nephritis, 89
Nervous Depression, 90
Neurasthenia, 91

Obesity, 92
Old Age, 93
Osteoporosis, 94

Phosphate Loss, 95
Pneumonia (see Influenza), 95
Postoperative Convalescence (see Convalescence), 95
Pregnancy, 96
Purpura, 96

Rheumatism (chronic), 97
Rickets, 98

Salmonella, 99
Senescence (see Old Age), 99
Slimming Diet, 99
Stomach, or Hiatus Hernia, 100
Stomach (sluggishness of), 101

Tonsilitis, 102
Tuberculosis, 103
Typhoid Fever (see Salmonella), 104

Urates (excess of), 104
Urinary Stones, 105
Urticaria, 105

Dr. E. A. Maury, now retired, was a general practitioner, an acupuncture specialist, and a homeopathist. He claims a tremendously high success rate among the patients he has treated with wine.

This book was a bestseller on the continent of Europe, first appearing in French and later translated into English and published in Great Britain. Dr. Maury is the author of ten other books on various aspects of medicine.

Dr. Maury was graduated from the Faculté de Médecine de Paris and was at one time the resident Specialist at the Royal Homeopathic Hospital in London. Before retiring, Dr. Maury practiced medicine for forty-five years and was considered a leading practitioner of homeopathic medicine in both England and France. He is also a lover of good wines.

Julius Jacobs, author of the chapter on American wines, is a recognized wine authority and a writer as well. He is the American editor for the London publication *Wine and Spirits*. He has represented several California wineries and has written for both consumer and trade publications on wine for many years. Mr. Jacobs has been on the staff of the Wine Institute, located in San Francisco, for over a dozen years. He presently lives in San Francisco, the heart of America's wine country.